HOW TO
MAKE MONEY
FROM
IDEAS
AND
INVENTIONS

R ROGERS

KOGAN
PAGE

First published in 1992

Kogan Page Limited
120 Pentonville Road
London N1 9JN

British Library Cataloguing in Publication Data

A CIP record for this book is available from the British Library.

ISBN 0-7494-0599-6

Typeset by DP Photosetting, Aylesbury, Bucks
Printed and bound in Great Britain by
Clays Limited, St Ives plc

Contents

1   Making a Start

Of all the great money-making inventions, both past and present, there exists two types of idea:

1. Those that make the inventor great wealth and fame.
2. Those that make fortunes for third parties or companies other than the inventor.

Some past inventors never lived to reap the rewards of their efforts, although the few that did often received riches beyond their wildest dreams. Walter Hunt, the inventor of the safety-pin, sold his rights to the invention for $10 to pay off a gambling debt.

Many examples also exist of inventors or manufacturers who have improved a product to such an extent that they have captured the market and become household names. Percy Shaw achieved this by designing the self-cleaning 'cat's eye', thus eliminating the need to remove them from the road for cleaning. He went on to make a fortune running into millions.

Percy Shaw was actually looking for the idea when it came to him by chance. He owned a company that manufactured reflective devices for the road, and was spending vast sums on having them periodically removed for cleaning. While driving home one evening in the dark, the headlights of his car caught on to a cat sitting in the road. The cat blinked and Percy Shaw's life changed. Some might say that his invention was inspired, but would a connection between his product and the cat have shown itself if he had not been looking for it?

Sometimes a winning idea can just seem to fall into your lap, so to speak. Take the case of the travelling farm equipment salesman touring the USA who came across a farmer who had invented a safety razor. The salesman's name was Gillette, and we all know what he achieved.

Again I wonder if Mr Gillette would have realised the importance of the idea he stumbled across if he had not been looking for something to change his life. Many people confronted with a similar situation would not even have bothered to let it register, being too busy earning a living.

My first invention did not come by accident either, in as much as I had decided to find an idea to make myself some money. I had had enough of being poor, didn't know any rich widows and wasn't prepared to rob a bank. I knew that all I would need was *one* good idea and, like Percy Shaw, my whole life could be changed. Maybe I wouldn't find the really great idea, but at least I was prepared to give it a try.

If you too would like to make money from ideas and inventions you must be prepared to try. The *first rule of innovation* is:

Make a conscious decision to think of a new idea and act on it.

It doesn't matter in what area your ideas are, the aim is to come up with and exploit fresh ideas or improvements. By doing so, not only will you enhance your own life, but that of others as well.

You get nothing for nothing in this world, so unless you are prepared to put some effort into your endeavours you may as well not start. I'm not saying that thinking of new ideas should become a full-time occupation, far from it. It is important to carry on with your day-to-day living while keeping your mind open to positive thoughts and suggestions. Take the case of the bird watcher who spends his weekends in pursuit of his hobby. When he's doing something else, he doesn't switch off. Even when driving somewhere important his subconscious is ever alert to the surroundings. A rare bird caught in a glance would immediately register in his consciousness and take over his actions.

Inventing is very similar in some respects because ideas generally come when least expected and when your concentration is elsewhere. Maybe this indicates that the subconscious is more inventive by inclination than the conscious mind. Nevertheless, once a conscious decision has been reached to find a new idea, the subconscious often takes over and gets to work on your behalf.

When I first started looking for a new idea, many daft, perhaps silly ideas passed through my mind, even that idea that attacks every inventor from time to time – the perpetual motion machine. Out of interest, applying for a patent on such machines has been banned by most patent offices throughout the world, having been labelled an impossibility. However, if you do think of such a machine, I would be pleased to see it. Patent officers are not inventors, otherwise they would know the most important truth with regards to new inventions:

Invention is the art of taking the impossible or the improbable and making it work.

An expert in a particular field will often tell an innovator that his ideas won't work, or his theory is wrong. This is because an expert is trained to think in a straight line, by the book. Anything that doesn't fit is wrong. If you think that you've got a good idea then you must satisfy yourself that it will not work before discarding it. There's nothing worse than rejecting an idea on someone else's advice, only to see it six months later on *Tomorrow's World*. I know, because it happened to me three times.

Many of you may already have ideas or inventions in mind. Some may be fresh while others may have been put away for future use. Nevertheless, for those starting from scratch, I shall assume that no ideas exist at all.

2   Starting from Scratch

The keys to innovation

Recognise problems

Humans are by nature an inventive species, and innovation is a part of our character. Most of our everyday items have been born out of necessity, hence the saying, necessity is the mother of invention. If this is so, then that necessity is the result of a problem that has been encountered. If this wasn't the case then we would still be living in caves, wearing skins and eating each other. This brings me to my *second rule of innovation*:

Recognise a problem that exists.

Most of us when faced with a problem can overcome it, either by ourselves or with the help of others. It is seeing the problem that is often the difficulty. How many times have you struggled over a job or chore? How often has someone else said, 'I wish there was an easier way'? How many times have you been aware that a problem actually existed?

There is always room for improvement in a product and there is always room for new products and new ideas. *Observation* and *alertness* are the keys to innovation. It could be a chance remark, or a story in the papers, that starts off your endeavours. Maybe a TV story will highlight a problem that exists.

Some of my ideas have come from the most unlikely sources. For example, one of my products, the 'Permanut', was invented after a friend had explained a series of events that happened to him. The friend in question had bought a new padlock and hasp set for his driveway gates, to stop his car being stolen. After securing these to the gates, he quite happily retired to bed, content in the knowledge that all was well. Imagine his frustration when in the morning he found that someone had removed the fixing bolts from the hasp and stolen it, along with the padlock. Clearly, here was a problem waiting to be overcome, and a product waiting to be invented.

Take a look at the solution that I came up with. Maybe you could find an alternative solution. Why not try it as an exercise?

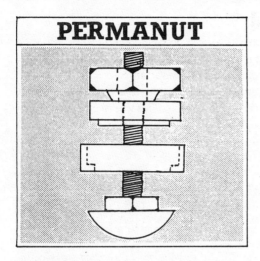

- Nut can be snapped off at a predetermined torque, leaving threaded sleeve securely in place.
- Final result leaves only a case-hardened collar making removal extremely time consuming.
- Ideal for lock-back plates, fencing, highway furniture, bench tools, safety guards, machinery and all situations where a more 'permanut' fixture is required.

Whatever the situation, whether talking to a friend or listening to the radio, as soon as you become aware that a problem exists, whatever it may be, there are two options open to you:

1. Continue with whatever you are doing and forget all that you have seen or heard.
2. Decide to remember the problem that you have encountered so that you may find out if this is the opportunity that you have been looking for.

Keep notes of problems

Assuming that you wish to be rich and successful, and are therefore prepared to put some effort into getting there, this brings me to my *third rule of innovation*:

Make a note of any and all ideas that come to you.

This is essential because it is easy to forget a moment's insight after a hard day's work, or after being distracted by one of the many daily events that are an integral part of modern life. I've done it myself. I know that there are at least six good ideas that I've noticed and then subsequently forgotten. It can drive you crazy trying to remember, so get into the habit of making those little notes, or carry a tape recorder with you. It only takes a small reminder to get you back on to the right track. When I became aware of the padlock/hasp problem, I simply wrote (padlock/hasp insecure), and it was enough.

It is not essential at this stage to dwell upon the problem, merely to recognise and make a note of its existence. You will find that if you follow this advice, you will soon have many pieces of paper, any one of which may contain the germ of a good idea or invention.

It may be that your first idea is the one that will succeed, but more often than not this is not the case. However, having a few ideas or options (in note form) in front of you will enable you to 'take the pick of the crop'.

Avoid becoming attached to one problem

One of the *biggest* mistakes made by inventors is to become *too attached* to an idea, causing it to become an obsession. You must resist this at all costs. Knowing when to let go of something and start afresh is of the utmost importance.

I once went to a business seminar all about marketing where each of us present had to put our business idea on to a piece of card in front of us. This was to enable everyone present to evaluate each other's ideas. We then had to discover our neighbour's proposal and in turn stand up and explain our neighbour's plans. This was a good way of stopping us from waffling on about our own pet project.

The two chaps next to me had put on their card, 'greengrocers', and after listening to them I stood up and started explaining about this great business plan the two chaps had. Before I had quite finished, I looked down and noted that the card had been changed to read 'cafe proprietor'. Clearly, they had changed their minds while I had been talking. Needless to say, everyone thought it a great laugh, which I must admit I did at the time. However, upon reflection I admire what they did, because rejecting an idea that you've previously convinced yourself is great takes a lot of courage, but it is something that must be done ruthlessly on occasions.

If an idea becomes successful, then becoming attached is inevitable, but until that happens be prepared to let go.

Work fast

Remember my Permanut invention. This was sold to a company who later found out that it had already been invented abroad, and so they dropped it. The loss to me was £10 patents fee and £5 development costs. That idea made me over £3,000 and I never had to leave the house. If you always expect your idea *not to be new*, then you *won't be disappointed* if it isn't.

I once invented a device to stop heavily loaded carrier-bags from cutting into the fingers and offered the idea to a company. Both myself and the company had searched to make sure that the idea was a new one and everyone was satisfied that it was. The company had agreed to make an advance payment and the terms were settled. However, as a test, the Managing Director decided to try the device out on some of his female workers, purely to get their response. The first person it was shown to promptly pulled a similar device from her handbag, explaining that she had bought it the week before in the far reaches of Scotland. Obviously, the deal fell through, but this brings me to my *fourth rule of innovation*:

Work fast in the initial stages.

It is a fact that if an idea or invention is the result of a problem that exists, then for the idea to be successful the problem must exist throughout society at that time. The obvious side-effect of this is that there may be more than one person engaged in overcoming the same problem at the same time but in different places. Unfortunately, whoever gets their idea registered first by way of patent or copyright or registered design will in all probability end up being the owner of the concept, or design.

If you discover that your idea has been preceded, it may be wise to do as I would, drop that particular idea. Obviously, if you precede the other party, you could continue while notifying them of their infringement of your right. Look at it this way, *if you can have one idea, then you can have another, and another, and another.*

Know when to move on

There is only one way to achieve real success from inventing ideas and inventions using my system, and that is to progress through the various stages explained until one of two things happen:

1. The idea becomes successful.
2. The idea ceases to be a viable proposition.

Whatever the outcome of a particular idea, it is important that the whole process be carried out at little or no cost to the inventor.

If at some time the idea falls into group two, ie, it ceases to be viable, the decision to abandon the project and restart must be taken without a backwards glance. What I normally do is to try to evaluate the potential of the idea, ie, the rewards that could be generated, and then, based on that, set a limit to the amount I am prepared to spend, or indeed gamble on that idea. If I find that the amount calculated doesn't seem to be achieving my aims, then either the product is not as viable as I first thought or it is under-capitalised and needs more input.

This process is rather like owning a shop. When you first start you have to put in time and effort to build up the business. Once it has built up you can start to take the profits from the business to improve your life-style. However, if after a few years the business passes its peak, you may have to start taking out less. At that point, if you have become possessive about your business, you may start putting back the profits made in the past to keep it going. Alternatively, before that happens, you could look for another shop that hasn't yet reached its peak and sell the first to someone else. It's just a case of *knowing when to let go or move on.*

Unlike a shop, or most other businesses, when you sell an invention you normally keep on getting an ongoing royalty for many years ahead.

Knowing when to move on may be just as important when your idea or product falls into group 1, ie, it becomes successful. It might be that your very success in itself becomes a risk. An example that comes to my mind is the story of someone I know whom I shall refer to for illustrative purposes as Fred.

Case study: Fred's tale

Note: No guarantee can be extended as to the total accuracy of 'Fred's tale', as with the passage of time a degree of embellishment is bound to have occurred.

Fred had a great idea. He had just been on a coach trip and had noticed that the luggage compartment on the coach was only half-full. (Travellers were allowed to carry three large suitcases but in fact rarely took more than one.) He realised that these coaches were travelling to fixed destinations and at fixed timetables all over the UK.

First, he approached the coach owners and explained his idea. He would put parcels on to the coaches, taking up the unused luggage space, and have them collected at the coaches' destinations. For this, the coach company would receive a fixed payment for each parcel. The coach operators loved the idea and agreed to participate.

Next, Fred contacted a cab company at each of the coaches' destinations to arrange for a taxi to deliver the parcels from the coaches to their delivery address at a fixed rate per parcel.

Offices were found near to London's Victoria Station and Fred was in business.

Following advertisements offering same day delivery (at a really competitive price), the company was inundated with work, so much so that the company had to purchase its own vans to deliver the overflow of parcels that couldn't fit into the coaches' luggage compartments.

Time passed and in due course Fred was approached by another larger parcels company with a buy-out offer of £250,000. Fred refused this offer, stating that it was his baby and he wouldn't part with it for any amount. However, he did agree, at a price of course, to allow this company to take over the massive overflow of goods that he was by then handling.

Time passed by and the business grew. Then, another company, which was much larger than the first one that had approached him with a buy-out offer, offered to buy Fred out for £500,000, an offer which Fred once again refused, explaining that he already had a good business and that he was contracted to another company to deliver his overflow. Within days, this company had bought out Fred's contracted partners and had obtained the rights to deliver Fred's excess parcels for itself.

The business carried on much as before with little outward change, excepting that by now the excess deliveries had grown considerably and many more vans were needed to cope with demand.

Time passed and in due course a third company, possibly the biggest in the UK, asked Fred what he wanted for his company. Once again Fred refused to consider any offer, explaining that he liked what he was doing and had already turned down an offer of £500,000 from someone else. An offer was made. Fred would receive £1.2 million for the business and a guaranteed job as overall Managing Director for as long as he wished. The potential purchasers explained that whatever Fred decided, they intended to obtain what they wanted somehow, and he should consider very carefully any refusal. Fred stuck to his guns and turned down the offer.

Within a few weeks the building from which Fred was operating was purchased by this company and Fred was out on his ear. The coach operators changed allegiance to the new owners and Fred ended up with nothing!

The whole point about this tale is that for one moment in time Fred had the opportunity of becoming a very wealthy man, but blew it. He may never have another good idea as long as he lives, and could regret his actions for the rest of his life.

It is important to realise that a small business can very rarely take on one of the 'big boys', and this applies to inventions as well. If you invent a product and it becomes too big for you, you must know when to pass it on to those who have more resources than yourself. It might seem important to 'hold on to your baby' but financial security would enable you to produce fresh ideas with less risk. *Your aim is to become rich and successful*. It doesn't matter if you reach that goal with a jet engine, or a teaspoon; it is only the outcome that is important.

As to which ideas are good and which are not, there are no hard and fast rules. Sometimes, what you think is a poor idea will be acclaimed by others, while an idea that you find more appealing may have little success. Who would have thought that a doll reported to have been born on a 'cabbage patch', or a rock described as a pet, could have been winners, but they were!

It often seems that those really great ideas that seem to appear everywhere overnight are instant successes, but this is often not the case. Many of them took years to become a success, and a lot of work to boot. An example of this is Rubik's Cube. It seemed as if it did not exist one day and it was a world-wide craze the next. In fact, it was invented years before, but did not take off because it was not known about and was not understood. In fact, the cube was turned down by the leading UK games manufacturer as something that kids wouldn't understand, and also something that would never catch on.

3 Getting Your Product Right

Categories of invention

There are many different categories of new invention or product, and focusing your attention on a specific type beforehand can sometimes be a real help in attaining successful conclusions. By having certain criteria in mind, you can choose those ideas that fulfil these criteria and reject those that don't, instead of roaming willy-nilly back and forth.

You could be inventing a product aimed at a specific age group. If so, then remember that each age group will have its own particular problems to overcome. For example, if you decided to invent a product for the elderly, you would have to decide what benefits the elderly would be interested in. You may decide that the elderly would prefer something to make life easier. That being the case you would have to decide if your idea or invention is to be targeted at a specific social group, or indeed at the whole spectrum of elderly. Ask yourself these questions:

- What would the elderly like?
- What would adults like?
- What would teenagers like?
- What would children like?

Remember that the elderly purchase for themselves and as gifts for the other groups, as do all groups, therefore a product could be aimed at one group but targeted at another.

The price of your product will also be a factor in how it is developed. Is it aimed at the rich? The working class? Or at the poor?

What benefits do you want your invention to offer? Do you want it to:

- make life easier;
- help make money;
- help save money;
- save time?

All of these are valuable benefits, depending on which group you are aiming at. Clearly, a rich business executive would be prepared to pay more for an invention or an idea that saves valuable time than someone without a job, who may prefer an idea that saves money instead.

Many other categories of invention also exist – for example, types of product or areas of application. It could be that your invention is based on certain skills or knowledge that you have, which you can use. If you are an electronics expert, then an electronics product may be the best choice, whereas a locksmith may be able to invent a new security system. Even a hobby or pastime can give birth to a real winning idea. A case in point is the lawn-raker, which was invented by a keen gardener, not by a tool manufacturer.

The options are endless when it comes to inventing new ideas and the limits are only the limitations of your own mind.

Conceive it . . . Believe it . . . Achieve it

Benefits or features?

Some products or inventions offer benefits to all ages and all sectors of society; however, do not confuse benefits with features. A *benefit* is what the invention or product offers, whereas a *feature* is how it works or is made. For example, a feature of a spy-hole fitted to a door is that it has a wide angle of view, whereas a benefit is the fact that it offers more security and peace of mind to the user. *It is usually the benefits that sell a product not the features.*

Some inventions seem to have no benefits whatsoever, but upon closer inspection they more than likely do. The yo-yo is a prime example of this. In appearance it does nothing except go up and down. However, it does keep children's or teenagers' hands and minds occupied, thus stopping boredom, two benefits in themselves which while not being used to promote the product are obvious in use.

When discussing your ideas with others be sure to talk more about the benefits than the features, as this will normally elicit a better response.

Another point to remember is that people generally fall into two groups: those who find it easier to learn and understand ideas by what they see, and those that understand easier by what they read. How you describe the benefits and features of your ideas or inventions should take into account the type of person that you are dealing with. Some will respond far better to an actual working device or graphic description while others will want every fine detail explained for their own evaluation. In plain English, some like pictures while others prefer technical descriptions. If you want to prove this to yourself, just visit any local electrical retailer and see what is happening. Some customers will be looking purely at the physical appearance of the product while others will be asking for specifications.

Making a choice

Whatever area your ideas are in, at some time you will have to choose the idea that you are going to work on.

Some people are quite capable of thinking about and doing several things at one time while others need to be totally free from distractions to concentrate. Whichever group you fall into, it is important at every stage to give your mind a chance to work to its best ability. When you feel that the time is right, look at the various ideas that you have written down and decide after careful consideration which one to pursue first.

Having decided on an idea, based on a problem that you have recognised, there is an important question that needs to be answered. *Is the problem that you have recognised a problem that exists for others, or have you created a problem in your own mind that is not really a problem at all?* The last thing you want to do is to invent a product that no one else wants or needs.

If your idea is an improvement to an existing product, then the question is easy to answer. All you have to do is to examine the existing market to evaluate the amount of business that similar or related products might generate. However, a degree of caution is advisable for three reasons:

1. If you have not protected your improvement(s), it is vital to maintain secrecy about the actual improvement(s) to be made, or the problem that caused you to come up with the improvement(s). If you put the problem into someone else's mind, this person may come up with the same solution, or some other, and pre-empt you in formulating your patent protection.
2. Consumers are reluctant to change their supplier, especially if it is already established, even though your product may be superior to the existing version.
3. Although products may be in the shops on a grand scale, their actual daily sales may be minimal. Take the case of the humble lawn-mower. Thousands of shops stock them because they sell related products, and a shop without stock is worse than useless, but how many are actually sold in a day?

It may be that an improvement, once protected, is best offered to an existing manufacturer looking for an edge over its competitors.

If your idea or invention is totally new, the question as to whether the idea is needed or not becomes even harder to answer. One way to evaluate the potential of an idea is to talk to others but *without giving away your intentions.* Bring the problem into everyday conversation and find out what the response is, being careful not to make a big thing of it, in case the game is given away.

Is it new?

This is a question that you will have to answer when you have chosen your idea, and there are different ways of finding out, depending on how you want to go about it.

It may be that you can afford to employ the services of a skilled patent agent to conduct a search of all previous patents held at the Patent Office in London, as well as at some libraries. Bear in mind, however, that there are millions of patents and a search can be expensive, especially when you consider that each country has its own records. Also bear in mind that many patents are still in the application stage, which means that no one can have access to them for 18 months. Thus, a similar invention to your own, invented and protected within the previous 18 months, would precede yours. This may not apply if your idea differs from that which is in the application stage (see Chapter 4).

As an alternative, you could, provided time was available, conduct your own search.

Various libraries around the country hold records of the last 20 years' patents for just this purpose. Your search may not be as effective as an agent's, but it would, if finance was a problem, serve as a good indication of your idea's uniqueness. When you think of the millions of patents waiting to be searched, you may feel that conducting your own search is rather a daunting task; however, it is not as difficult as it sounds. Fortunately, patents are recorded according to their area of application. Thus, you will only be searching those products that fall within your category. For example, if you invented a new lock, you would only have to search among the lock section for each year's records.

Sometimes the hardest thing to do is to find a category that your idea falls into for your search. To assist in this, a book of catchwords is held along with the patents. You have only to find the catchword that most fits your idea or invention and then search the sections in each year book that apply to that catchword.

Another way of researching the newness of your ideas is to question others but without giving away your intentions. If, for example, your invention or idea was to stop padlocks from being removed, you might visit a retailer of such devices and ask to see the range of products. After looking at the various padlocks, you could innocently mention that, in your opinion, fixing the hasp with standard nuts and bolts was risky. The retailer may then show you a different product that overcomes your objections to the first product. If this product and its price are all right, you may then decide to abandon your idea and to work on a different project. On the other hand, if the product is complex or expensive, you may decide that you could invent a cheaper or simpler device, provided there was a market for it.

It is worth asking the retailer if he is aware of any other products that fulfil your requirements, and if so, where they can be seen.

It is also worthwhile, during the conversation, asking quite innocently if the retailer sells many of the devices, and if not, whether it is because they aren't very effective, or because they are too dear, or because there isn't a need for them.

You may be told by someone that a product similar to the one you are thinking of inventing existed years ago. But is it possible for the person to remember something possibly from half a lifetime ago, or is it the person's memory playing tricks on him? I once travelled 50 miles to see a product that a friend said was identical to the one that I had invented to find that no such product existed.

If a product did exist in the past it may be worthwhile re-inventing it. Yale did this with the cylinder lock, which was invented in principle by the ancient Egyptians.

Product, time and place

There are three factors which make for a successful idea. They are:

The right product . . . at the right time . . . in the right place

If you believe that you have got the right product, at the right time, but are getting nowhere, you may well be in the wrong place at that time. In this context, place does not mean a geographical location, but rather an imaginary place where a real golden opportunity exists for you and your ideas at that time. There will always be someone interested in what you are offering; it is just a case of finding out where they are and how to get to them. *It's up to you to find those opportunities; no one else will do it for you.*

It could be that you have the right idea, at the right place, but the time is wrong. I once invented an anti-theft device for cars. It was a detachable signplate that locked on to the vehicle's number plate when it was parked. The sign, saying, 'Stolen If Moving', could be unlocked with a key and removed by the owner, prior to moving the vehicle. The idea was licensed to a manufacturing company and I received £5,000 in royalties from the first year's sales.

After a year, a large international company became interested in the product and approached me with a view to taking it over. After speaking to the licensees, I discovered that they had failed to pay the patent fees when due and so the idea was no longer protected in this respect. I still had copyright protection, which was sufficient for my needs but not for the new company. In any event, they pulled out and I revoked my agreement with the licensee. The product then remained on the shelf while I was working on other ideas. Eventually, I did try to resurrect it, but during the shelf period, numerous other anti-theft devices had appeared and my device was only one of many. I still sell some of the devices, mainly to caravan owners, but not in any great numbers.

This illustrates the importance of realising that the *factors that once made an idea feasible may no longer apply at a later stage.* It also illustrates the importance of *policing all licence agreements to make sure that patents are kept up to date.*

If, after careful consideration, you decide to continue with a project, and you believe that potential exists, you will want to stop the idea from being copied or stolen. You may in fact wish to do this before researching the idea, especially if it is only possible to research by direct questioning of parties who may be interested in the idea at a later stage, or if the idea is complex and requires the opinions of others to discover its feasibility. A good rule I always follow is: *protect first and ask questions later.* I believe that it is worth, say, two hours spent in writing a patent specification and a £15 fee to be able to act with total confidence. (The fee to complete the second stage (Form 9), see page 20, is now £120, and Form 10 £130.) OK, so I have sent off a few applications that have amounted to nothing, but in my opinion that is better than giving away a good idea.

4 Protecting Your Product

There are various types of protection available, depending on the type of idea being protected. The options available are: patent, copyright or design registration. When reading information in this book, on different types of protection, bear in mind that it is only a guide. No responsibility for the use or misuse of the information can be accepted by either the Author or the Publishers. Your final protection should be drafted with the assistance of someone professionally skilled.

Patents

Provided your idea is patentable, lodging a patent application will give you the option of pursuing full patent protection in over 60 countries. This option lasts for a one-year period dated from the moment that your application is received at the Patent Office in London. Should you decide to pursue it, either in the country of origin or elsewhere, you will be expected to take the application to the next stage before the one-year period expires. Some extensions to this time are allowed, but only under exceptional circumstances.

A patent remains secret for 18 months, during which time it can be withdrawn and refiled to get a new 18-month period , provided the invention has been kept secret or only disclosed in confidence in the period between refilings. This rule is to allow inventors to lodge their idea and then to have a period for improving and developing it, without the risk of intellectual theft. However, by refiling the inventor takes the risk that someone else may file an application for the same invention between the two filings, in which case the latter will precede the inventor's second application although it may not have preceded the first if it had been pursued.

At the end of the 18-month period, your patent application will be published for all to inspect, assuming that you have pursued your application to the next stage before the one-year option has expired. If, however, during the 18-month period, you have withdrawn your application, either because the idea was impracticable or because a new application was lodged, then the older version will not be published and its date of receipt at the Patent Office will not apply in respect of any claim by you as to the date from which your patent rights started.

It is important that you study all these points, so that you know exactly what your rights are.

What is patentable?

If your invention is capable of industrial application, is new, involves an innovative step and is not excluded as are some special cases, then it may be patentable.

Industrial application

An invention is capable of industrial application if it can be made or used in any kind of industry, including agriculture. However, some inventions, in particular, methods of treatment of the human or animal body by surgery or therapy or of diagnosis practised on the human or animal body, are classed as being incapable of industrial application.

Newness

An invention is said to be new if, after looking at all known inventions, patents, publications and descriptions of the then-known technology, the invention in its entirety is unknown. For example, if your invention was a star-headed screwdriver, then it would be considered new, even though other types of screwdrivers existed previously, provided that none of them had the total features of your invention, ie, the star-headed head.

Innovative step

This means that *if someone else skilled within the area with which your invention is concerned found your solution to the problem obvious, then an innovative step would not exist.* For example, an electrician faced with an overheating boiler might well fit a thermostat or thermal cut-out to the appliance. This would be an obvious solution and therefore unpatentable. If, however, some new and unobvious solution was employed by him, then that would be patentable.

Special cases

Any invention involving national security or of a military nature would need special permission for protection to be granted. In any event, any such idea could not be protected abroad without first being lodged at the Patent Office, of the inventor's country of origin for at least a six-week period, and then only after permission has been granted.

Any idea or invention considered illegal or morally offensive would be excluded from patent protection.

How to formulate a patent application

Before you can be afforded patent protection you will have to submit a specification to the Patent Office. The specification consists of a description and a set of claims. An abstract version (see page 23) will also have to be submitted within a specific period.

Description

The description is the most important part of the application and it *must* include as much detail as possible about your invention. It is the *concept* that you will be trying to protect. If you study the chart on page 79, you will see that describing concepts and formulating descriptions is not really that difficult. It is important to follow the very strict guidelines on layout, although if your application does not initially comply with these you are allocated a time in which to do this.

If you leave something out of your description, you will *not* be allowed to add it once the description has been received at the Patent Office, although you could include any new features in a fresh application which also includes the entire text of the earlier application along with the new features that need to be protected. This is provided the one-year option on the earlier application has not expired.

You can, if you wish, declare the date of your first application as the date from which you want your second or subsequent application to date, but only if a single concept unites them all, and provided the one-year option has not expired. An example of this is my Protectolock and Rampton Lock shown in the diagram.

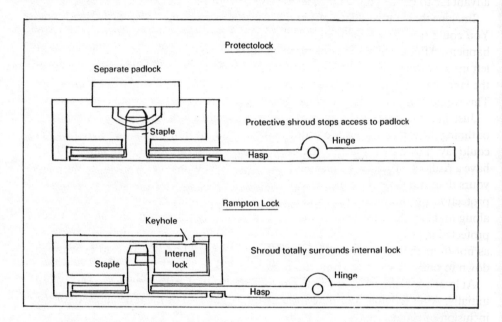

The first invention, the Protectolock, was described in a patent application that was lodged on 3 November 1981. This device, as you can see, was devised to stop a padlock's most vulnerable parts from being attacked with a saw or bolt-croppers. I then decided to incorporate a lock into the device, to put a lid on to the shroud, so to speak. I called this device the Rampton Lock, which was described in a new patent application lodged on 17 February 1982. Because the interlocking concept of the two devices remained the same, they were both later united into a single patent description and a full patent was issued.

The drawings shown here were those produced in the final stages when the product became viable, although the words have been added for the purposes of this book. The original drawings done by myself were more primitive. Initially, it is more important to include all details than it is to produce a masterpiece. The Patent Office allows a substantial period for tidying-up exercises and will let you know the date by which any such work needs to be done.

Soon after sending in your application, you will receive details of any mistakes in your preparation and the time allocated for rectification. You will only be told of mistakes in the format of the application, not the content. Only *you* can make sure that the content is correct.

Claims

Imagine that your idea is a plot of land with boundary fences. Your claims will have to distinguish your plot of land from all other plots that lie outside or around your plot. They will have to do this by means of clearly defined written statements. It is to your advantage to define your claims, ie, the size of your plot, as broadly as possible.

Imagine that you don't actually know what land you own, or where your land ends. You could say, 'I own the land as far as the eye can see', and then wait to see what happens. After a while, someone turns up and tells you that he owns the land to your left up to your garden path. If he could prove this fact, you would then say, 'I own all the land that I can see except on the left up to the garden path', and so on, and so on. This would continue until you knew exactly what you owned and what others owned.

Just like the deeds for a plot of land, your claims would consist of statements outlining the extent of your protection as far as your invention goes. For example, you could say, 'I own the rights to a "padlock"', whereupon someone else might say. 'I too have a padlock protected'. You could then say, 'Yes, but my padlock has features that yours does not have', and the person's response could be, 'Well, you must base your protection on those features', and quite rightly so. Someone else might then come along and say that the features included in your protection contain one previously protected in advance of yours. You would then modify your protection, ie, claims, so as not to include that feature. It has been known for 20 or 30 claims to be whittled down to one or two by the time full protection was granted.

At least one claim must be defined in your application, although this is not required initially. After lodging your description, you will be told of the time allowed for the inclusion of claims.

To determine your claims, a series of searches will have to be conducted by the Patent Office of all known claims, a service for which you will have to pay. Fortunately, this does not need doing until the end of the one-year period, and only then if you have decided to continue with your application.

The abstract

The abstract comprises a summary of your description in not more than 150 words. It must not include any drawings, but may refer to a drawing in the description.

Preparing a patent application

There are many books available on preparing patents. They are available from some main libraries. The Patent Office, Cardiff Road, Newport, Gwent NP9 1RH, will send you *How to Prepare a UK Patent Application* free on request, as well as other publications. See page 110.

An example of a professionally produced version of a patent application for a push-

SAFETY SEAT-BELTS

This invention relates to vehicle seat-belts.

Seat-belts are well-known devices designed to secure persons into a vehicle.

On the one hand, different cars have different types of seat-belt fitted. On the other, the only person really proficient in operating a seat-belt is the driver of that particular vehicle. Often passengers, in particular, the old, infirm and the young, have to ask for assistance to remove the seat-belts.

In a crash, these people would not be able to remove themselves after impact, and if a risk of fire occurred, then the ensuing panic would only increase the difficulties.

In order to overcome these difficulties, a seat-belt is adapted to be released remotely by the driver, while still being able to be released in the normal manner.

To help to understand the invention, a drawing is included.

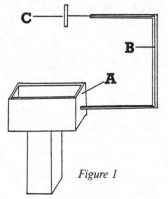

Figure 1

Fig. 1 shows a seat-belt socket A having a cable B going from the socket to a remote handle C.

The cable could pass through the vehicle's body and re-enter elsewhere, the handle being located near to the driver, in a convenient place.

Alternatively, the cable may stay within the vehicle, running along the vehicle floor.

More than one cable may be fitted to the handle, if preferred.

The invention may be adapted to be used within an aeroplane or coach.

In an alternative adaption the handle could be located on the back of one of the front seats, thus making it easier for passengers to release themselves.

button telephone lock is given on pages 84–9. This specification was produced at a cost in excess of £500. My original DIY application did not include any claims, or an abstract, but consisted of a description, with drawings, the application form and the £15 application fee.

When you receive the booklet *How to Prepare a UK Patent Application*, you may find the regulations daunting, but if you examine my first application opposite for safety seat-belts you will see how easy it is to formulate an initial application.

After studying the chart and specification on pages 79 and 80, you will probably be able to avoid the expense of a skilled patent agent initially. Of course, if your invention is very complex, you may wish to employ an agent anyway, from the start.

When preparing your patent application, include information even if you think it is irrelevant, in case your designs change as you progress.

Always keep copies of your specification for two reasons:

1. If you continue with the invention and make an improved version, you can add the new information to the tail end of your copy and send in the whole package in a fresh application. This will avoid having to retype the whole document.
2. Your designs are subject to copyright protection, which may offer certain benefits at a later stage (see below).

Copyright

If you are unsure whether an idea is patentable, it may still be worth applying, even though at a later stage the application may not be pursued. Applying for a patent and sending in your description *proves* that you thought of that particular idea at a certain time, which can be useful if someone else brings out the idea later.

Suppose, for example, that you invent and protect a push-button telephone lock, but for financial reasons fail to pursue the patent. If, as well as sending in the description with the application, you had kept copies of your original drawings and put them away for safe keeping, you would in effect have copyright protection. If someone else then invents a lock, based on the concept that you described in your application, that person may, if he copied your pictorial description, infringe the copyright that is associated with your original drawings. Even if there were no infringement of copyright and the other person's product became a success, he couldn't stop you from selling your copyright to his competitors, even if the two designs were similar.

Someone else's patent *cannot* stop you from producing a product if you can *prove* that you were producing the product prior to that person's patent being applied for, even if you do not have a patent in force. The patentees could stop another party from producing their protected product, but not if you sold your rights to that other party under a Copyright Licensing Agreement.

Copyright applies to original literary, dramatic, musical and artistic works, published editions of works, sound recordings, films and other types of artistic works. It also applies to technical drawings, or any other written material, that can be said to be original. This means that any original design or drawing that you do is protected by copyright. If someone else 1,000 miles away produced the same design or drawing, without having seen your version, then that person would also have copyright protection and would not be infringing your copyright. Mind you, at the end of the day, a court may well decide that one of you has preference over the other.

In my opinion, copyright can have distinct advantages over patent protection. It is free, it is automatic and it lasts for longer than a patent. A patent usually lasts for 20 years, whereas copyright lasts for the life of the creator plus 50 years. This means that copyright automatically passes to the creator's beneficiaries.

The easiest way to establish copyright is to mail copies of your original work to yourself, via registered post, making sure that the post office stamps all the joins in the envelope, prior to posting. Once received, the package should not be opened, but put in a secure place. In the event that a court of law requires proof of your copyright, the package can be opened by the court at that time. The postage date will establish the date of your copyright.

Copyright may be used to protect ideas that are in themselves incapable of copyright. For example, if you have two-dimensional drawings of a product, then no one after having seen them would be able to produce a three-dimensional representation from your two-dimensional drawings. This would be an infringement of copyright.

Designing a package, or leaflet, or instruction manual, that either shows the product or uses words to describe it can also give a degree of protection. How can someone else make your product if they can't promote it in a brochure without infringing your copyright? This is especially useful if you have a product that cannot, without great difficulty, be changed and still work effectively. In this event, drawings may well suffice to protect it.

Design registration

You can apply for a registered design provided your product/item has *eye appeal* and is not wholly functional. Patents can take up to four years to progress, whereas a design can be registered and granted within three to six months. The process is described in *Design Registration*, available free from the Designs Registry, Patent Office, Chartist Tower, Upper Dock Street, Newport, Gwent NP9 1DW. Design protection in general in the UK is described in another booklet, *Designs – Basic Facts*.

In order to qualify, the design must be different from any other design previously registered. While design registration is not considered to have the strength of a patent, it is far cheaper to get to a grant status.

You must apply for design registration before any items are offered for sale, and before any details of your design are published.

You will have the option of applying for registration in other countries for six months, provided that you have applied in your country of origin first. This option is effective from the date of publication of any material relating to the product/item, or from the date that it was offered for sale.

From the legal point of view, a patent application may be considered as prior publication; therefore, if you decide to apply for a patent and then later decide to register the design, the six months' option on the design will lapse six months after the patent application was received at the Patent Office.

Design registration may last for up to 15 years.

Patent agents

You may seek advice from a patent agent at any time if money is no object. What I do if I am unsure of the degree of protection that I have afforded myself, after lodging an application, is to produce a simple but explanatory model of the invention. I then visit a patent agent and ask if I have covered my invention sufficiently with my initial application. Normally, I find that I have covered it far more than even the patent agent would have. This is because I know all the different aspects of the invention and can include variations that might not be obvious to the patent agent. Don't forget that *you* are the inventor and an agent can *only* describe what you tell him.

Doing it yourself means that you can avoid the cost of the agent having to spend his expensive time learning about your invention. If you turn up with your idea, then the time spent by the agent in formulating your specification will be in the hands of the gods – while most patent agents are fair and honest, there will be the odd one who will try to take advantage of your ignorance. Having your ready-made application with you will enable you to judge how much time was spent on it, if indeed any time was needed at all.

I once filed an application and then visited an agent to have it evaluated. He informed me that the drawings needed improving, at which I instructed him to proceed. Some time later I was told that new drawings had been lodged at the Patent Office and I was sent a bill for £600, the cost of producing them. When I saw the new drawings, they were exact copies of my own original drawings in every detail. Needless to say I never paid that bill, and, eventually, it was resolved to my satisfaction.

Normally, the first visit to a patent agent is free, so get as much information and advice as possible then. When you telephone for an appointment, ask if the initial interview is free. In any event, most agents offer a reduced rate for private inventors as opposed to companies.

5 Negotiating Powers

It is important to realise that whatever form of protection you use, your negotiating powers with companies will be based on that protection.

If you send off copies of your protection to half a dozen companies, offering your idea, you may find that the invention gets modified and is in effect stolen, as in the following example.

My friend's company had been approached by an inventor with an idea for a new product. The inventor explained that he had only shown the idea and patent specification to one other company six months ago and that he had not heard from them since that time. My friend liked the product and agreed to take it on, and a date was set for an exchange of agreements. The day before the signing, my friend received a brochure through his door advertising a range of products. One of them was a slightly altered version of the invention he was due to sign up on the next day. The product was being made by the company that the inventor had visited six months before. In this instance the idea was dropped and the inventor lost out.

Inventing is a gamble, just as any business is, but there are ways of decreasing the odds against you, as I did in the following incident.

When I visited a large national company with an idea and the chief designer asked to see my patent specification, I refused, explaining that unless his company was prepared to license the product from me, then the content or quality of my protection was not their affair. He then asked me for my application number, which again I refused. Then he told me that his company could easily change my design and make their own. I laughed and told him that I would love them to do just that. 'Look', I said, 'I have protected the invention, and 15 variations of it. The contents of my protection will remain secret for 18 months. If you want to take the risk that your design is not the same as one of my variations, then I suggest you go ahead.' I added, 'Not only this, but every week I am going to lodge a fresh application outlining other variations as I come up with them.' I continued, 'Quite apart from this, it will be a whole lot easier for me if someone does steal the idea. For me to make the idea a success, I will have to work really hard for at least two years and spend large sums of money in the process. I will have to set up manufacturing equipment, pay for tools, employ staff, promote the product, employ salespeople, and market the product quite substantially. Even then I would have no guarantee of success. If you steal the idea and spend all your money, time and hard work on making it a success, and I take you to court and win, I will have succeeded without having to work for it. Not only this, but I will probably end up with more money in damages than I could actually make from the product. As for the cost of suing', I added, 'I have a barrister who will work on a percentage of the damages if

I win, and nothing if I lose.' Needless to say the idea wasn't stolen.

Part of the risk of inventing is that someone will steal your ideas. However, you must look upon any such act as a part of the game. If you win, you are rich, if you lose, you start again!

Of course, you could, if a company stole your idea, visit them and explain that you have a patent lodged, or copyright on the idea. Tell them that you intend to let them continue selling the product, *on your behalf*, and then take them to court once the product is established. They might tell you to get lost, but from there on in they will always be wondering whether they are working for themselves or for you. Alternatively, you could offer them a licence. It's better for them to be safe than sorry. Everything is negotiable.

When dealing with a company, bear in mind that provided you keep the contents of your protection to yourself, as is your right, then a DIY specification should be sufficient. If you show the contents of your protection to a company, they may well try to find a way round it, instead of reaching an agreement with you. If they have no knowledge of the content, then that situation cannot arise. It should be enough to show the idea and to state that you have taken steps to protect it. The company should then agree that once they have signed to take on the product, further protection should be done at their expense.

6 Designing a Product

The key steps

Before you can protect your device, you will have to design it. One way of doing this is to have something in front of you that is related to the object that you are trying to invent. Trying, for example, to invent a vehicle anti-theft device without access to a vehicle would be most difficult. What I would do, and you may follow my example, is to examine fully the area of application of my idea. In this case I would look in the car, under the car and around the car. These actions can often produce the inspired thought that will lead to the solution.

Putting yourself into the shoes of the person that the product is aimed at can also have the desired effect. For example, when I wanted to invent a telephone-related device for the blind, I actually blindfolded myself and spent two hours using the telephone to discover the precise nature of the problem. By doing this, I discovered that the problem was not that the telephone keys were too small, as everyone had previously thought, but that a blind person, if distracted for a second when dialling, would lose or forget his position on the telephone keyboard. A different problem had emerged and therefore a different answer was needed. This highlights the need to *make sure that you are working on the correct problem before you start.*

Once again, it is important to write down or draw anything that comes to mind as soon as possible. By doing this, if you have to stop for some reason, getting started again will not be as difficult.

When you feel that you have found the solution or solutions, make detailed drawings to enable you to see the whole device more clearly.

Having drawn the device, there are some questions that will have to be answered:

1. How will it work?
2. How difficult will it be to make and is there an easier solution?

If you are dealing with a new concept, you must understand it before you continue. You may have designed a product that works in principle but not in practice. By studying your drawings and your theories, you should be able to discover any inherent weaknesses in your designs, which you can then rectify. You must then repeat the exercise until you are fully satisfied.

It's very easy to complicate products with extra features that may not be necessary. The simplest solutions are the best, and a simpler solution may exist. It is important to look closely at your invention and if necessary start again. Look at your invention from the consumer's point of view. Is it easy to understand and simple to use?

Do not throw away any of your scrap drawings or notes. You may need them at a later stage for inclusion in your protection. Even if you do not use the earlier designs, including them in your protection will stop others from producing an inferior device to your own.

By following my advice to date, you will eventually end up with drawings of an invention based on an idea that you believe is original. You will also believe that it is not difficult to make, and you will be satisfied that there is not a simpler way of achieving the same result.

Statement of non-use

If you feel that your invention is likely to be thought of by someone else within a short time then protection is your first priority. If that is not the case you may wish to make, or have made, a working model of your invention, before protecting it, to reassure yourself that it really works!

If you are working on your own, keeping everything a secret is easy, so protection may not be as urgent. Of course, you may still decide to protect it as a form of insurance.

If you decide to discuss your ideas with another party, telling them that you are talking to them in confidence is one way of stopping them from repeating what you tell them without your permission. However, they must be told beforehand for it to be binding in law. It is no good telling them about your idea and then saying that it was in confidence.

Some companies, when dealing with inventors, insist that the inventor signs a document stating that any discussions are not in confidence; however, most will still insist that a patent is applied for before they see you, and in this event, your cover would be sufficient.

If you haven't protected your ideas and you wish to discuss them with others, insist that a statement of non-use is signed first. This is a legally binding document, an example of which is given on page 91. I've included a clause that covers the unlikely event of the person to whom you are talking being engaged on an invention identical to yours prior to seeing it. If they do not agree to sign, it may be wise to look for advice and assistance elsewhere.

7 Making a Prototype

How to go about it

Once you have protected your idea or invention to the best of your ability, you will have to make, or have made, a working prototype of the invention. There are various Enterprise/Innovation Centres around the country who may be willing to assist you in this. However, generally speaking, before they will help, they will want a patent search conducted to establish that the invention is new. Under some circumstances, they may conduct the search on your behalf, but in that event they will probably want paying. These centres can also offer advice on manufacturing and marketing of new ideas.

There are some drawbacks to using enterprise/innovation centres which you should know about before approaching them:

1. They may ask you to sign a document stating that, should your product become successful, payments would be made for work done. I myself think that this is fair, although you must find out *exactly* what it is going to cost you before committing yourself to signing such a document. After all, when is a product considered successful? When you've sold ten or when you have sold a thousand? Also, which jobs are chargeable?
2. These centres have quite an influx of ideas and so the choice of projects has to be selective. It may be based on personal preference, which is only human and unavoidable.
3. If a patent search shows that a similar idea existed in the past, they will take some convincing to continue with your idea. It may be that your idea is superior and worth continuing, so it is important to reach your own conclusions on your product's viability.

Even if your idea is accepted by a centre, you may have to go on to a waiting list, and three to six months could pass before work commences. Taking into account that a patent has to be pursued before the first year has expired, as well as the expense involved, clearly it is very important to have your product produced before that time to see if real potential exists. Thus, a wait of three to six months may be too long!

On the positive side, if your project fails, any money owed will more than likely be written off. Also, any advice given can be invaluable, and access to specialists is often available. If there is a lull in projects being worked on, you may get a prototype produced fairly quickly, and if it is, then quality will be superb. Industrial designers will often work hand in glove with you in the designing of your prototype, and even if the idea is very complex, either mechanically or electronically, their experts will be able to handle it. Remember, when you discuss your ideas with these people, it is usually in confidence and therefore protected.

As an alternative to enterprise/innovation centres, you may decide to have your prototype produced by a manufacturing company at your own expense. In this event, get at least six quotations and do *not* let any of the companies know what the others have quoted. Do not forget to set a value on what you are prepared to spend on the project before you start and do *not* go over it. If the quotes take you over the value, look for alternative methods, or alternative companies.

If finance is a real problem, or you are unsure of the viability of project, then why not share the risks and/or finance with someone else? A friend, or friend of a friend, may be willing to assist for a piece of the action. This help could be financial or by way of useful skills or knowledge. Often, a skilled, retired or redundant person will have time on their hands and a project to work on may be just what they are looking for 'to keep their hand in'. If the idea or invention is good, there will be plenty of people willing to help, provided you are prepared to share.

Declaration of trust

If you do find someone interested in assisting for a consideration, you do not want to be tied up with solicitors putting together an agreement; after all, the whole point is to do everything at little or no cost to yourself. But it is essential, when sharing your idea, that you maintain control of it; after all, it is your invention.

You can sell your rights to your idea if you wish, although in the long run it may be better to sell a proportion of the benefits of your idea. In effect, the latter means that you would have a partner or partners who would be entitled to a percentage of any monies that the idea generated, but in every other respect the idea would remain yours, and in your control.

To do this, both you and your partner or partners would become beneficiaries of a declaration of trust. This is a legally binding document, an example of which is given on page 92. You may use the document as given or have it altered by a solicitor to suit your requirements.

In essence, this document states that you, the inventor, declare that any money made from the named invention will be paid into a trust and distributed by the trustees to the beneficiaries according to the percentages written in. The amount that you are willing to sign away will depend on the product's potential, and the amount of work or finance being offered, but I would suggest that you never sign more than a total of 49 per cent away on any one idea. *Remember that once an agreement of this nature is signed, it is legally binding in law and cannot be revoked.*

I have used these agreements on many occasions in the past to raise finance and to solicit work or assistance without any complications arising.

Improvements

When you believe a product is finished or perfect, someone will often suggest an improvement or variation that you had not thought of. If the suggestion is really good, immediately revise your patent specification and submit a new one that covers the improvement or variation, as outlined in Chapter 4. It is not essential to adapt your prototype to bring it up to the new specification at this stage. The main thing is that you have protected the improvement before anyone else has a chance to beat you to it.

Above all, when considering improvements, *try to avoid the tendency to take away the simplicity of a good idea*, as may happen if you keep trying to improve your product further.

8 Making Your Product

Once you are satisfied that the prototype cannot be improved, there are three options open to you:

1. You may decide that the invention is not very good and that no real potential exists.
2. You may be pleased with the invention and decide to manufacture and market it yourself.
3. You may decide to find a company to manufacture and market it for you under licence, paying you a royalty for that benefit.

Scratching the product

If you decide to scratch the project, then moving on to a fresh idea must be done as a matter of course and without any regrets. If what you have done to date has cost you a lot of time and money, then you have not been following my advice. New products must arise at little or no cost to the inventor. Use other people's skills, technology and, if necessary, finance, and be prepared to give something in return. Remember that 100 per cent of an idea that can't be progressed is worthless, but 70 per cent of a finished article can be sold at a profit.

Manufacturing and marketing yourself

Deciding to manufacture and market your product yourself is a big step and should not be taken lightly; however, if you do decide to go this way, here are some pointers for you to consider.

Manufacturing

If you decide to patent your idea, rather than protect it with copyright or design registration, you will have to finance your patent through the various stages, which could run into a substantial amount.

You will have to work out any production methods that will be used and, unless you intend to work from home, you will have to find premises from which to base your production operations as well as staff to run them, both of which can involve a substantial outlay.

If your invention needs special tools or equipment, these will have to be designed and built. If you have components made elsewhere, you may have to pay for a special tool. In this event, care should be taken. Your choice of company may have to balance the cost of the tool against the cost of the component produced. One company may offer cheaper tooling with a dearer product, while another may do the reverse.

Also bear in mind that most companies that manufacture components have tooling done elsewhere and so are mainly concerned with profits made on the actual components. Some companies may have a department or subsidiary that produces tooling for them. In this event, you must beware of an expensive tooling price being made desirable by the offer of cheaper per item costs. It may be that work is required for the tooling department, so that at the end of the day the component could never be produced at the price quoted, or at least not in any quantities. Remember to get *all quotations in writing*, and insist that the maximum and minimum numbers of units that can be produced per week at the quoted price are included within the quotation.

Finally, remember that manufacturing is a skilled profession; you will have to satisfy many customers but you may also have to contend with getting paid late, or not at all.

Bank finance

If you need to raise finance from a bank to go into production, you should be totally convinced that the product is a real potential winner before you proceed. Most banks will want you to provide a business plan outlining exactly what you intend to do with their money, if they lend it to you. It will have to include all your estimated outgoing expenses and projected sales for at least a two-year period. The sample business plan on pages 94–9 shows you what is entailed. Although I know from personal experience that plans never work out as expected, because they do not allow for the unexpected, a good plan will, however, give a series of targets to aim for, which is what a bank manager will want to see.

If you do go to a bank, it will be looking for four things:

Customer . . . Purpose . . . Repayment . . . Security

It will ascertain these by asking questions like:

- Do you have the right character to start up in business?
- Do you have the right skills to do what you say you can do?
- What are you going to use the money for?
- Do you have any of your own capital?
- How profitable will your business be?
- How much money do you need?
- What will be the legal format of your business?
- Will you operate as a limited company, a sole trader or in partnership?
- How much competition is there?
- What will be the cost of the loan?
- Can your business afford the repayments?
- Do you have any security for the loan, such as a house or other property or shares?

Marketing

Once manufacturing and finance have been dealt with, the next thing you need to think about is marketing. *A classic mistake made by many is to think that a good idea will sell itself.* This is only true in exceptional circumstances. A product needs the support of experienced staff to market and promote it, which can in itself be a costly business.

Marketing is a subject on its own and could take up a dozen books. However, Chapter 11 gives some tips that may be of use. One thing is certain: if you decide to market yourself, a lot of hard work will be needed, and even then success isn't guaranteed. You may be better off trying to license a company to do all the work for you, and to pay you for the privilege.

Licensing a company

The first thing to do is to find a company that is interested in your product. Contacting companies that already manufacture similar or related products to your own can be productive, as can contacting companies that use manufacturing processes that would be used in the manufacture of your own product. For example, when I invented a push-button telephone lock made from die-cast zinc, I contacted a zinc moulding company rather than a lock company and reached a satisfactory agreement with them. In this way, I avoided my product having to compete with other similar products from the marketing angle and I guaranteed a 100 per cent commitment from the company.

Another way of finding companies is to visit one of the Enterprise/Innovation Centres. They often have a list of companies on their books who are looking for products. If they do find you a company, ask if you will be charged, *and if so, how much*, or if the company will be charged for the introduction.

When contacting companies, inform them that you are an inventor with a product, as this will usually open the right doors for you. All companies need an influx of ideas or new products and if the right product is offered they will be very keen to do business with you.

Most large companies will insist that you have a patent application lodged before they see you, to protect themselves from any possible conflicts that may arise at a later stage as regards ownership of an idea. You may be asked to sign a statement of non-confidentiality before they see you. This is to enable them to investigate the potential of your idea by talking to others without infringing your rights.

Provided a patent has been applied for, you should have sufficient protection. Here is a typical letter that I received from one of the large multi-nationals after approaching them.

Dear Sir

Thank you for contacting us about your idea. We are pleased that you thought of our company because a large part of our growth has always been as a result of developing new ideas. We investigate many ideas sent to us by private inventors.

Before you present your idea, could I suggest, if you have not already done so, that you consider obtaining legal advice. Your legal adviser will be able to tell you if your idea is patentable and, if so, indicate what steps are necessary to provide you with that protection.

To enable us to investigate your idea, we shall need a detailed written description with drawings or photograph. At this stage, please do not send us any models.

I will submit the information about your idea to those people in the company best able to evaluate it, and will notify you as soon as possible as to whether or not the company has an interest in your idea.

Could I please stress six points which are standard in our dealings with outside inventors:

1. *We will not accept anything that you send us 'in confidence' because that term has special legal meanings. In addition, a thorough study often requires the advice of several of our company staff and perhaps even prospective customers or others outside the company. To get their opinion, we may have to tell them about your idea.*
2. *We do not assume any obligation to advise whether or not your idea can be the subject of a patent, nor about the commercial possibilities of your idea.*
3. *We cannot consider any ideas you submit unless you are the owner of the invention. If others (for example, your employers) have rights, you should tell us who they are and what their interest is.*
4. *If you are under 18 years of age, we cannot deal with you without the written consent of your parent or guardian.*
5. *Any assistance in time or skill which you provide will be at your own expense.*
6. *We need your agreement to let us keep whatever material you submit for our records, and to be certain that our files correspond, ask that you keep copies of everything that you send.*

If you submit your invention to several companies for evaluation, it is wise to inform them of this and that it will be first come, first served. They will fully understand this. I have been to many large companies, Chubb, Union Locks, 3M, GEC, to name but a few, and I have always found them to be most helpful, even when no interest was forthcoming. 3M even treated me to a slap-up meal, while another company set me and my wife up in a country hotel for the weekend. There is no need to be afraid of these large companies. They are run by people, and most welcome inventors with open arms.

It will not matter if your prototype is made from card and string, so long as it works and the principles of the idea can be fully understood. Companies will realise that you are an inventor, not an engineer, and will generally have their own experts to study your concepts. A product in the shop may look nothing like the original prototype; it may have cost a substantial amount to get it to the retail stage.

If you submit your idea in writing, do *not* use the description and drawings from your patent application. These should remain secret to yourself at this stage. A simple outline of your invention, together with a three-dimensional drawing, should be enough.

Some companies may be quite slow in evaluating your ideas, and may ask you to come back at a later stage for further discussions. This should not matter if you have followed my advice and have other ideas on the go as well. I often have three or four ideas going at once; in fact, since I sent out drafts of this book in its original format to a number of publishers for their consideration I have invented four new products and have another three in mind, meanwhile, leaving my copy of the manuscript on the shelf until any interest was shown. You must realise that if you consistently spend all of your time running around with one idea, and those ideas fail, then the cost of your ideas in working hours will be considerable, with the result that you will not be making any money and may well end up vastly out of pocket. In fact, in the case of my book, so much time passed (18 months) before I received any replies that I had put it totally out of my mind. Nevertheless, it serves to show that, although real interest can take time to show itself, it can be well worth waiting for. Here are some extracts from a letter that I received:

We have read your proposal for your book and have found it most informative and interesting.

I feel that it could be a good book which we will be most interested in publishing.

This was clearly worth waiting 18 months for, and worth continuing with. Furthermore, regardless of whether I let that particular publisher have the rights, or some other, or if I indeed decided to publish myself, I could continue with that project knowing that there was one party to fall back on.

Smaller companies are also often on the look-out for new ideas and on the whole are much quicker to respond than the larger companies; however, they may not find it as important to live up to an image, and so care should be taken when dealing with them.

On one occasion when I was involved in discussing licensing terms with a smaller company, the managing director agreed to pay me a royalty of 5 per cent on the first 1,500 units sold, followed by a 2.5 per cent royalty on the remainder in every year of the term of the agreement. The royalty was to be paid on a quarterly basis. I made the mistake of allowing production to start before the actual agreement had been signed, and from thereon, every time I asked for the agreement, I was told that it was still being drafted. After three months the first appointed payment time arrived and I was told that the number of units sold was approximately 1,000. The selling price of each unit was £35 and I therefore worked out the royalty due in the following way:

First 1,000 units at 5 per cent of £35:   £1,750.00 due

Amount I received: £912.50

Difference: £837.50

When I queried this amount I was told that the company's interpretation of our agreement was 5 per cent on the first £1,000 input, not on the units sold.

This illustrates the importance of *not* making verbal agreements and insisting that an agreement is signed *before* anything is started. A verbal agreement is binding in law unless you state before discussions that everything discussed is not binding in law and is only by way of preliminary negotiations.

One inventor that I know of was offered £5,000 in cash for an idea and a job for life. He couldn't resist the offer and signed away his rights, letting the company draw up the agreement. Within eight weeks the company had liquidated itself and the rights had been passed to another company owned by the same person in lieu of an apparent outstanding bill. The inventor lost his job and his product. *The company made a fortune*, while he made only the original £5,000 and a few weeks' wages.

There are many risks involved when licensing a company and it is important to protect yourself from every eventuality. What I do these days is to turn up with an agreement already written, thus taking the initiative away from the company. I explain that it is my royalty agreement which they must agree to if they want my product. That's not to say that I've already decided on a royalty amount. That has to be negotiated each time an agreement is reached.

Royalty agreement

A royalty agreement will depend on the product's potential and the amount of time spent on development. Never part with your rights for a percentage of the profits, as it is too easy for a company not to make a profit, even though substantial sales may have been made. You only have to look at the amount of money coming into your own house. How much is left at the end of the year?

A royalty agreement should give the company the rights to manufacture and market your invention in return for payments to you. The company should be responsible for any patent fees, and it should agree that any improvements belong to you and will be subject to the same agreement.

A good agreement should protect you from every eventuality, ie, the company going bust, or changing ownership, or failing to pay you on time. It should also stop the company from producing another product in competition to your own, and many other things besides.

A sample royalty agreement is given on page 101. You may use this in its entirety or have it modified by your solicitor to suit your own requirements. (You could get a solicitor to draw up an agreement, but this would cost a fortune, even if he knew what to put in it.) If your idea is subject to copyright as opposed to patent protection, then substitute the word 'copyright' for 'patent' in the agreement. I have used this agreement on many occasions and it has never let me down.

What's an idea worth?

When you visit companies, they will probably ask you what you think the retail value of the end product is likely to be. If you value your product too cheaply, its development will be restricted to producing a cheap product, which may make it unrealistic to produce. Furthermore, a manufacturer will be more interested in a product with a higher profit margin than one with no profit at all.

With a new idea, finding its value can be a guessing game to start with. For example, if you show an unknown product to 100 people, they will each put a different value on it. Even business and marketing experts do not really have a clue, as my experience illustrates.

I once took a product to a large company for evaluating and at the end of the meeting we ended up with a proposed retail price of £5 per unit. This company had over 5,000 products at the time and the person I was talking to was an 'expert'. Following our meeting, I returned home to await developments. I had not been home for more than ten minutes when the expert telephoned and informed me that on reflection he felt that the retail price should be £10. This happened three more times before the day was out. The product ended up being valued at £18 per unit. In fact, I did not end up going with that company, but my product remained at £18 per unit. This shows the difficulty involved in valuing a new product.

In the past, the method used to find the value of a product was to add a percentage to the manufacturing costs for profit and then to sell at that price; however, this does not take into account one important fact:

The value of a product is the value of the job it does or the time it saves, not the cost of production.

Fifty pence-worth of plastic would be worth £10 if it saved you £20.

The real value of a product may be attributed to *one* feature of that product, as opposed to the whole. As long as that one feature gives a benefit then the product will have value. For example, this book was inspired by one paragraph in another book that cost £15. The contents of that book were totally useless to me, and excepting for that one paragraph, I never used it at all. I rate the value of that one paragraph far beyond the price paid for the complete book. Look at this book. If it inspires you to conceive, believe and achieve, then how can you put a real value on it? What is the value of knowledge?

Whatever your ideas, mechanical, electronic, artistic, musical, designing or whatever, do not under-value what you are offering. If it originated from within your own mind it is *priceless*.

NIH syndrome

NIH, 'Not Invented Here', syndrome can show itself as a wall of resistance to your ideas or inventions. It often happens when dealing with research and development personnel, frustrated inventors or failing business owners. You will hear them say, 'It won't work', or 'It won't catch on', or 'It's a daft idea', or 'I thought of it years ago'.

Constructive criticism is all right, and may in fact be very useful, but NIH can be destructive if you allow it to affect what you are doing. When you receive criticism, try to establish if it is real and genuine, or just NIH rearing its ugly head. It can break out at any time, and is basically a form of jealousy tinged with frustration. It could be that the person using you as a target can sense your impending success and is riddled with envy. I received the following reply from a well-known TV rental company after I approached them with one of my products:

> *We have now looked at your sample product and would like to draw your attention to the following point:*
>
> *When fitted to plugs intended to be used with an extension socket, the product could act as a lever to pull the plug out. This could happen if someone kicks the socket and the product catches the floor. In view of this point we cannot consider your product.*

I wonder if the writer realised that within six months of receiving his letter I would sell over 300,000 units of that particular product, many of them being used in extension sockets, and without one complaint.

In another reply I received, the following internal memo was included. Obviously, I wasn't meant to see it, let alone receive it.

> *Dear xxxx,*
>
> *Enclosed is a letter that I received from an inventor, outlining a product that he has developed. I do not understand how it works, and am too busy to reply. Could you please draft a letter with some regulations, the usual thing, and send him off a reply.*
>
> *Thanking you*
>
> *Dave*

This is the actual reply I received:

> *I feel that your idea while being perhaps novel* (he did not understand it either) *would need to be carefully reviewed by you in the light of government regulations concerning the permission to connect such attachments to public telephone lines.*
>
> *Let me say at the offset that I am not in a position to affect any rulings in this area, and that products for which I am responsible have to comply with the same regulations.*
>
> *These regulations are administered by OFTEL, via the BAB for telecommunications BABT, and originate in committees of the BSI.*
>
> *I am returning your documents should you feel it worthwhile approaching them.*
>
> *Yours*
>
> *xxxx*

Clearly, if you receive such responses you will have to decide if they are genuine or just simply NIH.

Spin-offs

One invention will often lead to a whole range of products, each being related to the first. It may be that all of them are good; however, the cost of launching a range of products will be considerably higher than launching a single product.

If manufacturing yourself, it may be wise to concentrate on one spin-off at a time, bringing others out as each one becomes established. Of course, if the products are simple and cheap to produce this may not be necessary.

If a company has been licensed to manufacture and market your invention, do not offer the company any others until the first is on its way. If you do, you may find that the resources of the company are divided, with each product having less time and finance spent on it. In other words, do not put all your eggs in one basket, at any one time.

9 How I Invented the Identiplug and Associated Products

Having read this book so far, you may be wondering how to put it all together, and where to start. In this chapter, I show how I actually put all my advice to use after the beginning of the book (excepting for some minor adjustments) was finished.

You will see how I thought of specific ideas, and how they progressed through the various stages, or were dropped.

You will see how I used the documents given in this book, and how I used other people's skills to assist me in making money both for myself and for them.

You will see how, whatever happens, it cost me very little to accomplish, just as your ideas and inventions should cost you as little as possible.

The Identiplug

Sometimes when you start on an invention you will find that it won't work for technical reasons. This does not mean that all is lost. Often, while working on one idea, another is born. My Identiplug invention is a good example of this.

I had decided to invent a device that could be attached to an electrical plug to indicate when the plug was live. The device would indicate this by means of a light. Although sockets and plugs were already available with an in-built neon light that would fulfil this function, I felt that the consumer would rather buy an add-on, as buying a replacement would mean throwing the whole unit away.

My invention consisted of two pieces of plastic sandwiched together, with two wires between. A neon was mounted on the outside of the device and was connected to the two wires. Three holes passed through the plastic in positions that corresponded to the three pins of a standard 13-amp three-pin plug.

Title: Illuminative plug attachment

Technical Field: This invention relates to electrical sockets.

Background: Electrical sockets are well known and of many different types. Some are available with in-built neon indicators that indicate when the socket is in the 'on' position.

Drawbacks: The cost of changing sockets in a building in order to achieve this end would be prohibitive and where this feature is desired by a visiting workman for example, changing the sockets would be impracticable on a temporary basis.

Essential Technical Features: According to the invention a device comprises at least two pieces of plastic or similar non-conductive material being sandwiched together to form a single piece. At least two holes pass through the device in positions that correspond to the layout of the electrical pins of a standard electrical plug. A neon indicator is fitted to the top of the device. Two internal wires located within and between the two pieces of plastic are connected to the neon at one end and at the other they protrude into the holes through which the 'live' and 'neutral' pins of the plug will pass.

Example: A specific example of the invention will now be described with reference to the accompanying drawings in which:

Fig. 1.   Shows the device in its entirety.
Fig. 2.   Shows the two pieces of material in exploded view with the location of the internal wires shown (dotted lines).

Referring to the drawing Fig. 1, the device comprises two pieces of plastic or similar material A and B sandwiched together. A neon C is mounted and fixed thereon. Three holes D pass through the device.

Referring to the drawing Fig. 2, internal wires E and F connect to the neon at one end and protrude into the 'live' G and 'neutral' H holes at the other end.

The example shown is of the 13-amp 3-pin type and therefore has a corresponding hole for the earth pin to pass through.

In use, the device is pushed on to the back of the plug, allowing the plug pins to pass through the holes. The internal wires make contact with the 'live' and 'neutral' pins of the plug and a circuit is made between those pins and the neon. If the current is switched off at the socket, the neon will go out and vice versa.

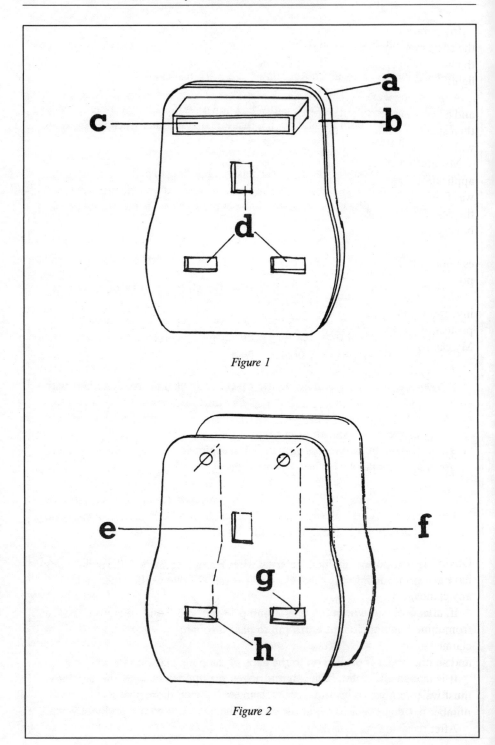

Figure 1

Figure 2

In operation, the device was attached to a plug, with the plug pins passing through the corresponding holes in the device. The two internal wires then made contact with the live and neutral pins of the plug and, provided the plug was live, the neon would light.

A prototype was made from pieces of plastic from a washing-up liquid container, and a neon was seconded from an unused socket. Having made sure that it worked, I then spent two hours drafting out a patent specification, which I duly sent off along with the £15 fee.

My first patent application was as shown on pages 45–6. The aim of my patent application was to protect my idea initially, so that I could then go on to discover if it was feasible. I was not concerned with the grammar, but with the content and getting the description right. A description should enable an expert in the area of application, having read it, to produce the invention from scratch.

I could have included the claims and abstract of the invention, but because it is not essential at this stage, I preferred to wait until I had investigated the product's potential.

However, if I had wanted to include the claims, I would have had to look at the invention and work out the technical features that were to form the basis of my protection, ie, the boundary fences around my property, putting my main claim first. My claims could have been as follows:

1. *A piece of plastic adapted with holes to allow it to be fitted to an electrical plug, the plug earth, live and neutral pins passing through the holes.*

2. *A piece of plastic as claimed in claim 1 having a second piece of plastic of similar shape fixed to the piece of plastic as claimed in claim 1 to form a sandwich.*

3. *A piece of plastic as claimed in claims 1 and 2 having a neon fixed to its surface.*

4. *A piece of plastic as claimed in claims 1, 2 and 3 having internal wires or similar conductive means.*

5. *A piece of plastic as claimed in claims 1, 2, 3 and 4 wherein internal electrical wires connected to a neon project at their other ends into the live and neutral holes as claimed in claim 1.*

Obviously, the number of claims would depend on the complexity of the invention. I have always felt it better to wait until a patent agent can be employed before lodging any claims.

If, after lodging my claims, another invention had come to light that was different from mine but consisted of a piece of plastic that fitted to an electrical plug's pins as claimed in claim 1, then that claim would be lost and I would have to rely on the others, and so on.

It is important to remember that proof of posting is not proof of invention. You must wait until you receive a receipt from the Patent Office giving your application number before publicising your ideas. This usually takes about seven days to arrive.

After receiving my patent application receipt, I decided to do some market research to test the viability of my idea. It was while doing this that I found that I had made a simple mistake in formulating my idea.

The plug that I had used with my invention, and with which it worked perfectly, was over two years old. However, an electrician to whom I showed the device explained that a new type of plug was coming on to the market and the older types were being phased out. After examining one of the new types of plug, I discovered that the live and neutral pins had been insulated half-way along their length. This meant that no electrical current could flow through my device, and so in effect it was useless.

I knew I would have to throw my idea away; however, as it looked good in use and operated in such a novel way, I was loath to discard it. I therefore made a conscious decision to take this piece of plastic and find another use for it.

Just as identifying a problem is the first step to overcoming that problem, deciding on an area in which to look for a problem can set the whole process off. Therefore, I started to look for other problems associated with electrical plugs and sockets. *Once you start looking, events that would normally pass you by take on a new significance.*

My home, like many others, suffered from too many appliances and insufficient sockets. This was especially difficult for the children to come to terms with, having to remove the toaster to use the microwave, and then having to remove the microwave to re-insert the fridge. Add to this a fryer, a sandwich maker and a portable TV, and the inevitable was bound to happen.

Returning home after a night away, I discovered that my son had removed the fridge plug the night before to use the toaster, and then replaced the toaster plug with the deep fat fryer plug. The fridge had defrosted, and the fryer had been cooking away all night.

Here was a situation that was not only expensive, a £20 loss of frozen food, but also highly dangerous, with the fryer almost melted. This looked like the problem I was searching for, and I decided to invent a product to overcome it.

Taking my earlier invention, I removed the neon and replaced it with the word 'fridge'. Pushed on to the back of the plug, this not only acted as an indicator of which plug to replace, but also enabled others to check that the correct plug was in fact plugged in.

I had at this point invented a Plug Indentification Tag as shown in use on page 44. While the PlugTag, as I called my new invention, located over the plug pins in the same way as my previous device, the concept was different and therefore a new patent application was needed. I had already wasted £15 on my original idea, but who could say which idea was destined to become a winner?

I realised that the device could fit many different types of plug, so the protection would have to take this into account. Through experiment, I also realised that the tags would have to grip the plug pins in order to stay in position when the plug was removed. Hence, I prepared my description, just as I had done with the previous invention, and sent it off to the Patent Office along with the fee.

By the time I received confirmation that it had arrived (about seven days), I had produced a dozen prototypes from bits of plastic, and used self-adhesive labels to produce the different tags. The titles ranged from fridge to kettle to toaster, etc.

Once I received my application number, I knew that secrecy was no longer essential, so I began to discuss my idea with others. While showing my prototypes to different people, I soon realised that I had come up with a really good idea. One friend suggested that a Braille version would be ideal for the blind community, since they either had to rely totally on memory to find out which appliance the plugs were connected to or had to trace electrical leads with their hands. Clearly, this was a great adaption. Since I had not included it in my patent specification, I took out the copy of my original description and typed at the base of it, 'The tags may also be adapted to include Braille, or any other symbolic language'. I then sent off this revised description as a fresh application with its £15 fee. This was done within half an hour of the variation's conception. In this respect, speed is of the utmost importance. The last thing you would want is for someone else to come up with a variation of your idea.

When filling in the application form, I declared the earlier application as a priority application, thereby backdating the new application to that date. The earlier application had in effect been superseded and would, if continued, be replaced by the new one.

I now had the protection covered and my next decision was whether to:

1.　offer it to a manufacturer; or
2.　manufacture and market it myself.

Because of the simplicity of the idea, I felt that the second option was worth pursuing, provided the cost was not prohibitive; after all, my golden rule is that the inventor should spend as little money as possible on developing ideas.

Following research, I decided that the plug tags would have to be injection moulded, and then either silk-screen printed or hot-foil printed with the different titles. For the inejction moulding a special tool would have to be made, and for the printing, special jigs to hold the tags would be needed.

Following enquiries, I received three quotations for the moulding tool and the cost of the actual moulded product:

	Tool cost	Cost per tag
Company 1	£12,000	5p
Company 2	£ 7,000	7p
Company 3	£ 5,000	5p

The time estimated for the production of the tool was six to eight weeks from receipt of order. Clearly, if I chose one of these companies, the product would never get off the ground. After visiting another two companies, I found one that was prepared to make a start-up tool for only £180 and would supply the tags at 2p each. A remarkable difference, wouldn't you agree!

After applying the same principles to the printing side, I found a printer who was prepared to finance the cost of the jigs, and to print the tags for 2p each.

I had decided that the tags would be sold in point-of-sale dispensers containing a range of over 50 titles, and these could be made for £5 each with initial artwork, etc, costing £250.

I also searched for, and found, a retired engineer who was willing to make a Braille embossing machine for another £250.

I now had the basic costs of setting up in business, although there were numerous other incidentals that had to be taken into account as well. I therefore prepared an itemised list showing what the real costs were likely to be:

Injection tool	£ 120
Stock of 10,000 tags at 2p each	£ 200
Printing of tags	£ 200
Dispensers (50)	£ 250
Artwork for above	£ 250
Braille machine	£ 250
Headed paper, order forms, invoices, business cards	£ 180
Brochures: design and production	£ 250
Envelopes, stamps, etc	£ 120
Subtotal	£1,820
VAT	£ 273
Total	£2,093

£2,093 was the first basic amount I needed.

I had decided to try manufacturing and marketing myself for an eight-month period, and if after that time I wasn't succeeding, I would then look for another company to take the project over, leaving me to continue with other ideas, as and when they came.

There were now other costs involved, ie, premises, rent, insurance, heating, telephone, fuel, wages, etc. I worked out that I would need another £5,000 pounds for this. The total needed now went up to:

Original amount	£2,093
Extras	£5,000
Total	£7,093

At this stage, I could have used my own money, or indeed the bank's as finance, but why should the inventor, having come up with the idea, also have to risk his own money as well!

Taking a leaf out of my own book, I approached two friends and asked them if they would be prepared to finance the project in return for a small share of any profits made. Asking several people is better than asking one, as it is easier to find a few people with a little than one person with a lot. In addition, someone putting in a lot would expect more in return than someone putting in a little.

My proposal was that they would finance the start-up expenses – in other words, pay the bills. This made it easier to reach an agreement as it showed that their input would be going into the product and not into my back pocket. I also explained that I would expect them to input any skills that they had free of charge when needed.

I explained that their interest would be purely monetary and that the agreement, which I had already formulated, would state that I would maintain total control. I was not selling a portion of the product, or my rights, but a proportion of any monies made by the product. I used the trust agreement on pages 92–3, to bind us contractually. In effect, I then had two silent partners.

One of my partners was a senior graphics designer for a large company and he immediately set to work designing letterheads, order forms, brochures and other associated items. This saved the company, which was by then called Identiplugs, considerable money. In addition, because my partner had a stake in the business, the quality of his work was superb.

I then visited the local council and enquired about premises and grants. A business plan was formulated and submitted to the grants department for evaluation and premises were found in an industrial complex.

The injection moulding tool and printing jigs were by now complete, as was the Braille machine, and I had received my first completed plug tags.

Following the adaptation of some of the tags to include Braille, I visited the local organisations for the blind and came away with orders totalling £2,000. Clearly, a good sign. By that time I had also received a £2,000 grant and was engaged in marketing the product.

Next, I found out that one of the companies exhibiting at the International Business Exhibition at Olympia in London was showing a high-tech device for the blind. It was in fact a device that could read written words and then, via a voice synthesiser, relate what it had read to the user. Following my approach to the company, it agreed to let me share its stand, free of charge, if I would provide some of my plug tags to give away as gifts to its clients.

By this time, the tags were being sold in various outlets at 33p each, and seemed to be doing quite well. I had also contacted various magazines, *Good Housekeeping*, *Popular Computing Weekly* and others, and managed to get features into quite a lot of them. I had even sold 40,000 tags to one magazine, and 80,000 to another, to be used as promotional products for their readers. This was a good way of achieving customer awareness and getting paid for it at the same time.

The date of the exhibition arrived and as promised I was allowed to share a stand. A great deal of interest was shown for the plug tags, although no orders were taken. However, as far as I was concerned, two things did occur that made the whole exercise worthwhile.

First, I was approached by a businessman from Ireland who was interested in marketing the plug tags in Ireland, on an exclusive basis. Following discussions, he agreed to pay me £5,000 per year for this privilege and to purchase substantial numbers of the plug tags as well. The £5,000 was payable in advance, annually. *The licensing agreement* on pages 101–9 was adapted and used as a contract between us.

Bearing in mind that I started with nothing but an idea, I now had the following completed and owed nothing:

1. Identiplugs UK set up
2. An injection moulding tool
3. A Braille machine
4. Printing jigs and artwork
5. Point-of-sale dispensers
6. One thousand brochures designed and printed
7. Letterheads, invoices, etc
8. Office equipment, computers, etc
9. Premises
10. A large stock of plug tags
11. Identiplugs Ireland set up

Instead of 100 per cent of nothing I now had 75 per cent of a viable proposition, and a few thousand pounds in the bank as well.

The second good thing that happened at the exhibition was that I was approached by a British Telecom engineer. After looking at the Braille plug tags, he explained that whoever designed them could, he felt, design other products for the blind. A particular problem that he had encountered for blind, elderly and handicapped people was the difficulty they all had when using push-button telephones. Some manufacturers had tried to overcome the problems by increasing the size of the keys or by embossing Braille on to them, but this did not seem to help a great deal. After listening with great interest, I consciously decided to have a closer look at the problem as soon as the exhibition ended.

The tactile telephone adaptor

Within six days, using the principles described in this book, I had designed, protected and produced a working sample of my new telephone device for the blind, partially sighted, elderly and handicapped.

Before another three weeks had passed, I had designed a brochure (see page 62), had an injection moulding tool made (at a cost of £120) and produced the first 1,000 products. They were costing me 3p to produce, and over 2,000 were sold within the first four weeks at £1.20 each. Over 1,000 were sold to British Telecom for their own distribution.

This product appeared on TV's *Tomorrow's World* in 1989 and has sold in quite large numbers since.

Braille identity cards

I had by now acquired a name for coming up with original ideas, and was duly approached by a blind organisation. They were having a meeting with the county police chiefs to establish whether the police would consider carrying Braille identity cards, for the benefit of the blind community in the country.

In theory, all that was needed was a plastic card with details embossed in Braille on it. However, such a card would have no novel features, as the solution was obvious, and was therefore unprotectable. This would mean that anyone could compete with me if the idea became successful. I therefore decided to produce a card with novel features that could be protected.

I examined a basic flat card embossed with Braille to find out if there were any potential problems. I found that if the card was placed alongside other cards in a wallet, friction and rubbing together would wear away the embossed dots of the Braille, making the card unreadable. The same thing would also occur to cards kept in a pocket.

Also, police officers, not being able to read Braille, would not know which way to present the card to the blind person, which while not being a great problem, could in itself be considered awkward.

To overcome these problems, I therefore designed a card with recesses in its surface, the braille being embossed within the recesses. This prevented wear and made it easy for the blind person to follow the lines of information. I also made the top edge of the card thicker, to identify the correct way up. The information for the sighted would be printed prior to the Braille being embossed.

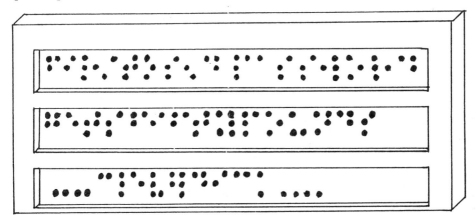

As it so happens, this particular idea has not yet been taken up, mainly because I have not yet got around to it, but I will, and then, who knows?

Concluding note

Some readers may be wondering how I found the time to finish this book, considering that I am also running a company and inventing new products continuously. The answer is simple: *use other people's abilities and don't be afraid to give something in return.*

In its original format, this book was finished over two years ago, when it was put on the shelf to await further interest. It is protected by copyright, which is free, and wasn't costing anything just sitting there. This book is in its own way an invention, in that I started with nothing and created a product worth money. I even employed my own methods from within the book in the actual formulation of it.

After receiving the letter from the publisher showing positive interest, I took the following course of action, realising that the time needed to finish it would be hard to find.

I had a friend who had helped me in the past to write letters to various companies. I knew that he was articulate and that he had a word-processor that he enjoyed using. I showed him the publisher's letter, as well as the original manuscript, and offered him a small percentage, if the book was successful, in return for his help. I would supply him with rough handwritten sheets and leave him to type, reorganise and re-present the finished article to me for my approval. The real advantage for me was that I could write page after page, without worrying about grammar or spelling, and meet him from time to time to see how it was going and to formulate the layout. In any event, he agreed and the trust agreement on pages 92–3 was used to bind us contractually.

This example shows that while greed may encourage us to go it alone, we can sometimes achieve more by involving others in our success. There are plenty of people willing to help, but you must be fair with them from the start, and be prepared to share a little of your success in return for the help received.

It is now 12 months since I started Identiplugs with that piece of humble plastic from a washing-up liquid container. I had quickly realised from the beginning that four distinct and separate markets for the product existed. I decided to let someone else take on what I considered to be the hardest market to establish. I therefore licensed another company to market the plug tags to the retail shop side of the business. For this, I receive a substantial yearly premium, as well as a royalty based on sales. I also get paid for printing the tags, which is now done at my own factory.

I kept the Braille, the mail-order and the promotional sales side of the business for myself. On my side of the business alone in one week, I made over £20,000 profit and the product continues to grow.

The tactile telephone adaptor is now in the official British Telecom guide for equipment for the handicapped, and is also selling well.

As for this book, the golden rule is that there are no golden rules. After consideration, I decided to publish myself and did so in a word-processed version. It was a financial success, but my main customer wanted a professional product, so I took it to a publisher after all.

I have invented, developed and produced all the products shown throughout this book and they have cost me very little. I have made many thousands of pounds in profit and will continue to do so.

You too can invent new ideas and products. All it takes is a little effort and the knowledge to put that effort to use.

10 Designing a Brochure

When designing your brochure it is important to realise that it is the window through which your product will be seen and initially evaluated. It is therefore worth spending a little time getting it right.

On the following pages are reproductions of the brochures that I have used for my own products. They have had to be reduced in size for reproduction in this book, but in the original, the plug on page 57 was actual size. Old addresses have been deleted. You will see that there are many different factors that go towards making a brochure effective. Each factor is as important as any other and each must be thought about carefully.

Just as I have tried to make this book interesting to you, you must also try to make your ideas and inventions interesting to others. Only then will the reader want to go past reading the brochure and contact you.

LARGE LETTERS *GRAB ATTENTION!*

CONTRASTING COLOURS GIVE MORE *IMPACT!*

SIMPLE DRAWING SHOWS PRODUCT IN USE!

Note how the use of words 'Unique' . . . 'New Product'
show that the product has not been seen before.

REVERSED PRINT explains product

**EXPLAINS WHY
PRODUCT WAS
INVENTED!**

**INFORMS OF HIGH
PROFIT POTENTIAL!**

**EXPLAINS PRODUCT'S
SIMPLICITY AND LOW
COST!**

**SHARES IDEA OF
SOCIAL BENEFITS!**

**PHOTOGRAPH SAVES
1,000 WORDS!**

**OFFERS A
COMPETITIVE EDGE**

**HINTS AT THREAT OF
COMPETITION!**

INTRODUCES COMPANY NAME!

LINKS REVERSE . . . KEEPS READER READING!

Here's a unique New Product that's bound to be a big hit with YOUR Customers....

PLUG IDENTIFICATION TAGS

Electrical Appliances are manufactured to very high safety standards nowadays, however, electrical accidents, particularly in the home, still happen!
An appliance, 'plugged in' by accident, is a real source of danger.

Identiplugs now offer a neat, simple and inexpensive way to help overcome the dangers of electrical accidents! Plug identification tags, a concept protected by world-wide patents, are such a simple yet extremely effective idea.

Manufactured to high standards, an identification tag simply slots onto a standard 13 amp plug and grips securely. The appliance is then 'instantly identified' by the name on the plug.

Electrical users benefit...

In the home, the office, the workshop: anywhere that electrical appliances are used. Identification tags are available with the names of almost all appliances in bold, neat red lettering.

Identiplugs even manufacture these tags in BRAILLE. Think of the benefits that this will bring to blind people.

The Electrical trade benefit...

Manufacturers can now supply an identitag with every appliance! This could make a big difference when a customer is choosing between two appliances of similar specification and price.
An identitag could 'clinch' the sale for the appliance that offers it!

Identitags are bound to be extremely popular so we offer special 'bulk purchase' discounts to wholesalers.
Identitags are only available from Identiplugs. Contact us today for further details and prices.

To assist Retailers, Identitags are supplied in a neat, attractive and distinctive display unit. This shows the whole range of Identitags and allows self selection.

Supplied at low unit cost, an excellent retailer mark-up can be made. And yet, Identitags will still be so attractively priced that many purchases will be impulse buys. After installing and using them, customers are bound to come back for more.

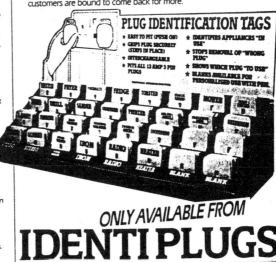

ONLY AVAILABLE FROM

IDENTIPLUGS

NOT ONLY THIS – BUT ALSO....

SEE OVER

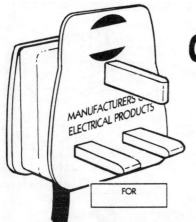

Customised Identitags
(printed on the reverse)
to promote your business, service and products...

A UNIQUE ADVERTISING MEDIUM!

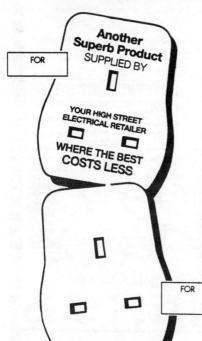

YOUR COMPANY NAME ... ALWAYS AT YOUR CUSTOMERS FINGERTIPS.

HAS INTRINSIC VALUE ...WILL BE USED FOR YEARS AND NOT SIMPLY THROWN AWAY.

CUSTOMISED TAGS TO SUIT YOUR COMPANY AND PRODUCTS OR SERVICES.

DESIGN SERVICE AVAILABLE ... OR PRINTED TO YOUR SPECIFICATION.

VERY LOW UNIT COST.

REAL BENEFIT AND VALUE TO THE USER.

A UNIQUE REMINDER EVERYTIME THE USER PULLS THE PLUG.

There's never been such a great opportunity to get your name into the home, permanently, discretely and at very low cost!

Printed on the reverse side of a standard identitag, your company name or message is seen every time customers use the appliance! Here's a very subtle, powerful, almost subliminal method to advertise to your customers.

Conceived as a free give-away, here's an opportunity for you to benefit from a unique advertising medium that's really too good to miss! ·

Contact us today for details and prices.

ONLY AVAILABLE FROM

PLUGS

YOUR COMPANY NAME – ALWAYS AT YOUR CUSTOMERS FINGERTIPS!

SHOWS VARIATION
IN USE!

VARIATION HEADING
AS *LARGE* AS MAIN
HEADING

GIVES PERSONAL
TOUCH

CONTRASTING
COLOURS ENHANCE
APPEARANCE!

REVERSED PRINT explains concept

SHOWS AT WHOM
PRODUCT IS AIMED!

EXPLAINS INTRINSIC
VALUES!

SHOWS OTHER USES!

OUTLINES
BENEFITS!

EXTENDS
EXCLUSIVITY!

COMPANY NAME ON BOTH SIDES!

FINAL SALES PITCH!

OFFERS IMPORTANT
BENEFIT!

SHOWS PRODUCT IN
USE!

LARGE LETTERS
INSTANTLY EXPLAIN PRODUCT!

INFORMS OF
SPECIAL FEATURE!

EXPLAINS WHO
PRODUCT IS FOR!

SHOWS VARIED
RANGE FULL SIZE!

OUTLINES EXISTING
PROBLEMS!

GIVES SOLUTION!

OFFERS CHOICE
TO CONSUMER!

COMPANY NAME INTRODUCED!

FINAL SALES PITCH!

PLUG IDENTIFICATION TAGS

PRINTED IN BRAILLE

FOR THE BLIND

PARTIALLY SIGHTED AND ELDERLY

Electrical Appliances are manufactured to a very high safety standard but still accidents happen! Particularly in the home.

Each day the risk of accidents increases as more appliances are used in the home creating more confusion. This is greater if you are Blind, Poorly Sighted or Elderly having to select the plug to switch on or off by touch or memory alone.

Plug Identification Tags are extremely effective. Printed black on yellow they are easily read by the Poorly Sighted and Elderly. Embossed with "Braille" they are just as easily read by the Blind.

The Tags simply push onto any standard 13amp 3 pin plug instantly identifying the appliance by the name on the Tag.

LARGE RANGE OF TITLES AVAILABLE

AMPLIFIER	DICTAPHONE	FAN HOOD	LAWN MOWER	SANDER
ANSWERPHONE	DISHWASHER	FOOD PROCESSOR	MICROWAVE	STANDARD LAMP
BEDROOM LAMP	DRILL	FAX	MODEM	SHREDDER
BLOW AMP	DISK DRIVE	FISH TANK	MUSIC CENTRE	STRIMMER
CLOCK RADIO	EXTENSION	GRINDER	MONITOR	TOASTER
COFFEE FILTER	ELECTRIC FIRE	HAIRDRYER	OVEN	TUMBLE DRYER
COFFEE MACHINE	ELECTRIC BLANKET	HOT PLATE	POWER TOOL	TELEVISION
COOKER	ELECTRIC SAW	HEATER	PUMP	TELEX
COMPUTER	FRIDGE	HEDGE TRIMMER	PHOTOCOPIER	TELEPHONE
CHARGER	FREEZER	KETTLE	RADIO	TYPEWRITER
CASSETTE PLAYER	FRIDGE/FREEZER	LAMP	READING LAMP	VIDEO
COMPACT DISC	FRYER	LATHE	ROUTER	VACUUM
	FOOD MIXER	LIGHT	STEREO	WASHING MACHINE

IDENTIPLUGS

AN ESSENTIAL AID TO SAFETY AT VERY LOW COST!

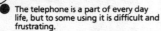

GIVES **ALL POSSIBLE USERS!**

SHOWS **THAT IDEA IS NEW!**

GIVES **BENEFIT**

SHOWS **PRODUCT IN USE!**

NAMES **PRODUCT**

EXPLODED **VIEW**

GIVES **REASON FOR INVENTION!**

EXPLAINS **CONCEPT!**

SHOWS **VARIATIONS!**

GIVES **BENEFITS!**

COMPANY NAME!

FINAL SALES PITCH!

Hints for designing your own brochure

1. Be bold when introducing your product.
2. Supply background information on why the product is necessary.
3. Always simplify your description of the product and how it works.
4. Try using colours and different typefaces to make it more readable.
5. Always explain the benefits to all possible users.
6. Include financial benefits.
7. Try to make an aspect of your product socially acceptable – this could lead to *free* publicity.
8. Always try to show an actual picture of the product, not an artist's impression.
9. Never assume that the main product will be the winner. Give all variations equal space and effort.
10. Keep variations separate while keeping the overall content connected.
11. Check for mistakes. Once it is sent out, it is *too* late for changes.

11 Marketing

Working out a marketing strategy

Marketing is best achieved by acting on a plan that has been made after research has been conducted, and then monitoring the overall effects. This process of research, planning and acting on your decisions is a continuous process, and in most businesses is in a constant state of change.

The concept of marketing isn't just flogging products. It goes much deeper than that. Marketing is:

- the business as seen by the customer;
- finding out what the customer needs;
- organising the business to satisfy those needs;
- communicating to the customer that you can satisfy those needs;
- doing it at a profit.

Marketing is all about getting the right goods in the right quantity to the right place, at the right time, at the right price, and making a profit. *Marketing is all about finding, getting and keeping customers.* A satisfied customer may tell six others, but a dissatisfied customer will tell far more.

Making a plan is no guarantee of success, although often the causes of failures are quite simple factors that could have been foreseen. These may include misunderstanding the market, not having enough money or failing to have clear objectives. By itself a plan won't overcome any of these common faults, but often the process of formulating a plan will ensure that weak points are identified early enough to make positive changes.

Imagine that you are baking a cake. The cake is your overall market strategy. It will consist of specific ingredients, comprising the products or service, the price being asked, the means of promoting the product or service, and the place at which it is to be sold. If you were working to a known recipe, everything would be easy; however, that is not the case, because every product or service will have a different mixture of ingredients. A cheap product like a cheap cake may not last very long, and could leave a bitter taste in the mouth. Offering a product for sale in the wrong place would be like offering cakes at a Weight Watchers class, a waste of time! Before you decide on the mixture of ingredients, some sort of research will have to be carried out:

- research to ensure that you have the right product;
- research to establish the correct price;
- research to find the best way of promoting the product;

- research to ensure that the product is offered at the right place, at the right price, at the right time, and to the right people.

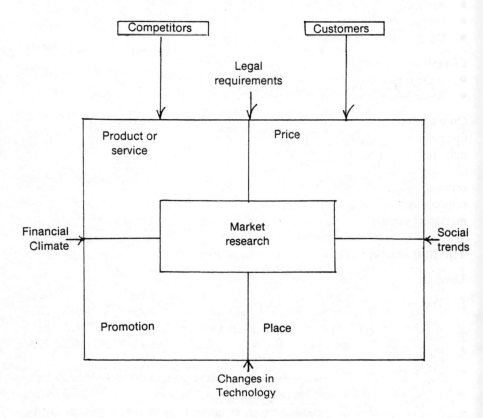

Figure 11.1 *The link between research and marketing decisions*

Figure 11.1 shows how research is unavoidably linked to all your decisions in marketing. It also shows some other considerations that will have to be taken into account when working out your strategy. Let us look at some of them:

Financial climate
- What can you afford to spend on the product?
- Do you need to look for finance?

Social trends
- Is there a group of consumers with similar tastes and needs at whom you can target your product or service?
- Who are they?
- How do you reach them?

Legal requirements
- Are there any regulations regarding the product's manufacturing processes?
- Are the goods being supplied reliable?
- Do they live up to their claims?
- Do they meet all safety regulations?

Changes in technology
- Is the product likely to be superseded by an improved version?
- Are others working on similar products or offering a similar service?

Once all these questions have been answered and your marketing package has been formulated, you will have to act on it and offer the product to your customers. You may have competitors offering their own products or services to your customers, having applied the same rules to their marketing strategy as yourself. Their mixture of product, price, promotion and place may differ from your own, and only market response will tell which is correct. Furthermore, as your business grows, so your marketing strategy will have to alter to meet changing climates.

The marketing concept

These are the rules that should be applied:

1. The concept: Producing what people want to buy; not selling what you want to make.
2. Putting the customer first: Organising your business so that this happens.
3. Finding out what the customer needs: Carrying out market research.
4. Finding satisfactions for those needs:
     Product – the right goods
     Price – at the right price
     Promotion – presented in the right way
     Place – through the right channels.

Let's look at each of the last four ingredients – product, price, promotion, place – in turn.

Product
The product that you offer for sale should be viewed as your starting point, because you will often need to carry out modifications or alterations to suit your customers. These may be to the product itself or the packaging. Of course, if your research was up to scratch in the beginning, such modifications may not be necessary.

Once you are established, you can afford to have it all your own way, but until that happens you must be prepared to bend to your customers' wishes. That doesn't mean that you can please all of the people all of the time, but that you should *try to please as many as possible.*

When I sent out the first 100 samples of my Braille plug tags asking for comments, I received quite a few orders and nothing but praise for the quality of the Braille. After a month, I received one letter stating that the Braille was terrible and needed modifying. Before changing it, I contacted other customers and asked for their opinions. All of them said that it shouldn't be changed. So I didn't. I lost one customer but kept all the others. If someone contacts you about a fault in your product, do not avoid the issue, and if necessary admit the fault. Ask the customer what he would like you to do to rectify it. Put the ball in his court!

I once sent out 300 Braille tags with 'lion' instead of 'iron' embossed on them, and 300 people had 'lions' on their 'irons'. I had to replace the whole lot, and because I managed to make a joke of it, my customer wasn't at all put out and we ended up as quite good friends.

It is always a good idea to ask customers for any suggestions regarding improvements, then if the product does not come up to their level of expectation, they will tell you why not, rather than just throwing your product away and not ordering. However, if an improvement is suggested, don't be tempted to run off and make the improvement straight away. Ask the customers if the improvement will clinch the sale, and then make your decision based on their answer.

Finally, try to get the product or company name right, because that in itself can be a valuable asset. When Freddy Laker went bust, he sold the name 'Sky Train' for over a million pounds . . . not bad.

Price

Discovering the true value of your product can be a nightmare, especially if it's unique and you have nothing to go on. Even so, some sort of research will point you in the right direction. Some big companies give a number of their products away and then, after a period, ask the end users to complete questionnaires outlining the product's usefulness and perceived value. Others find out what a similar type of product is being sold at and pitch their price a little lower, unless of course their product is far superior, in which case the opposite may apply. Another way of discovering the value of a product is by experimentation.

If you have invented and protected a product, and it is unique, then you can dictate exactly what to do with it. If you want to sell to one customer at £5 and ask another for £15, then it is up to you, and no one can complain. It is your idea and you have control of it.

This is how I arrived at a value for my plug tags. I visited one shop and left six packs of three tags to be sold at 99p per pack. I then visited another and left six packs to be sold at £1.20 per pack. Finally, a third shop sold the packs at 50p per pack. The packs at 50p never sold at all. The packs at £1.20 were sold, but fairly slowly, while the packs at 99p sold straight away. I therefore fixed a price on each plug tag of 35p and to date have had no complaints.

Just as you can't please everyone all of the time with your product, so you will not be able to with your price. *The price must be a careful balance of what you want, and what others are prepared to pay.*

Bear in mind that while a product may retail in the shops for £1, the shopkeeper will want to buy it from you at a price that allows for a fair profit margin. If you deal through wholesalers, they will want their percentage as well, before the shopkeeper even sees the product. Most shops work on a 33 per cent margin, while wholesalers may want 50 per cent or more. Do not fall into the trap of being held to ransom by the promise of large orders.

We all assume that the large buyers make large profits by buying in bulk at low costs. This is not always the case. The basic percentage may be quite low, but will often be built up by quantity discounts or by early settlement discounts. A good buyer will always ask you what you are offering as a trade discount and work from there. *Don't give away too much initially.* You can always offer a bit more if needed.

When discussing prices with a buyer at a large store, he asked what percentage I was offering, to which I replied 30 per cent. He asked for another 10 per cent for quantity and 2.5 per cent for early settlement, ending up with a profit margin of 42.5 per cent. If I had offered 40 per cent at the beginning, he would still have wanted to add on the same amounts, and I would have ended up with less profits for myself.

I know that the temptation is to give a higher percentage thinking that it will make a difference, but that is not true. If a company likes your product and believes that it will make money, it will agree to your terms. If a company does not like your product, nothing will induce it to buy.

All companies need new product lines to grow. However, as it is the job of the buyer to get as good a deal as possible, this may mean not showing too much enthusiasm towards your product. But remember that it is the buyer's job to buy and, at the end of the day, if he likes and needs your product then that is what he will do. What you must do is to present your product in such a light that it is your product that is bought. Do not expect an instantaneous response. It could take weeks or even months for an order to come through, and even then you may have to do a follow-up visit.

Promotion

How you present your product or service will depend on the type of product or service being offered. It may be that your product is small and cheap to produce, in which case you could send an actual sample with an accompanying letter. On the other hand, if it is complex or large, sending a photograph or brochure with details of the product and its benefits would suffice. Take care not to complicate your presentation, as it will become boring to the reader and he will quickly lose interest in it.

If you are presenting your product personally, practise what you are going to say beforehand, preferably with someone who is prepared to 'put you in the hot seat' with questions and objections. Also make sure that your product is fully operational. In this way, you will hopefully avoid slip-ups, unlike I did on the following occasion.

I once made a display from wood and mounted my products on to it. A handle was fixed to the top for easy carrying. Imagine my embarrassment when, after arriving for an appointment, the weight of the display had caused my fingers to swell and I couldn't remove them from the handle. A screwdriver had to be sent for to release me and needless to say I lost my edge and didn't get a sale . . . I couldn't stop laughing though.

The image that you present can be a vital consideration and you must always try to show confidence. Some of the bigger companies will want details of your trading background before dealing with you. In other words, they will want to know if you are credible.

With wholesalers, you can ask for space to promote your products to their customers in their premises, and then let them judge the response for themselves. Provided interest is shown, an order should not be difficult to extract.

Promoting through press releases is useful and can be quite easy to achieve. Newspapers and trade magazines need articles to fill up space, so provided you offer a well written article, leaving them as little to do as is possible, there is no reason why it should not be used. Always send press releases direct to the editor, since he will decide what will and will not go into a publication.

Finally, be generous with samples if you have to. If you appear as a penny-pincher your image will suffer.

Place

There are many places where your products can be sold. *The important point is to identify the markets you are aiming at and to find a means of reaching them.*

Selling direct either to shops or to the customer (door to door) can be very time consuming when balanced against the response. If your product is expensive, one or two sales a day will be worthwhile, but if it is cheap and cheerful that will never do.

It may be better to sell to wholesalers who can do the leg work for you. They will often have hundreds of customers and can get you up and running fairly quickly. However, when selling to wholesalers it is essential to work out a price structure before visiting them, as any hesitation in telling them what your prices are will result in your getting stuck in negotiating back and forth. It may be worthwhile offering some goods on sale or return, although goods which do not 'owe the wholesaler' money will not get as much attention as those that do.

Preparing and sending promotional brochures to shops can be productive, but you must be prepared to wait for a response. This could take up to a month or more, especially if the shopkeeper is busy, although in this case he will probably not be interested in new ideas or product lines anyway.

Mail-order may be another option, and if it works the rewards can be vast. Apart from the cost of advertising, all profits end up in your pocket.

You may be able to set up a merchandising operation with various magazines or periodicals. In this event, they will want a percentage of all orders received via their (free of charge) advertisement. Again, the response time may be quite slow, as my experience illustrates. Following an article in *Good Housekeeping* about one of my products, I didn't receive an order for over a month; however, they then came very fast and continued coming in for over 18 months afterwards.

Selling direct to specialist groups who will be interested in your product can also be very rewarding. If you do, try to get endorsements from someone within the group whose opinion others will respect. If they like what they see do not be afraid to ask for something to that effect in writing. It will be no end of help in opening other doors for you. Here are extracts from three letters that were written to me within ten minutes of my meetings with the group/organisations concerned. Finally, it is no good, after a meeting, wishing you had said a bit more, or been more enthusiastic about your product. Get excited before you go. Excitement is contagious.

You will find many books on marketing that go into far more detail than I do. After all, this book is primarily about inventing as a way of making money. You will also find thousands of experts ready to advise you. But do not forget that few, if any, of these so-called 'experts' have actually tried it out for themselves at their own risk. I have, and I have learnt a lot of lessons from the experience, so I hope that my few points are of use to you in your own endeavours.

NEWCASTLE
UPON TYNE
POLYTECHNIC

Head of Unit
Jim Sandhu

24th October 1988

Handicapped Persons Research Unit

Dear Mr Rogers

As one of the major R & D organisations in special needs in the UK and the only one to carry out evaluations for the Consumers Association we would like to endorse your tactile telephone aid. We believe it to be functionally useful for a wide range of disabilities.

Best of luck

Yours sincerely

Jim Sandhu

Gateshead Metropolitan Borough Council

AIRS

ACCESS TO INFORMATION AND READING SERVICES

Co-ordinator: Katherine Bowman

Central Library · Prince Consort Road
Gateshead · NE8 4LN
Tel 091 477 3478 Fax 091 477 7454

21st October 1988

Dear Mr Rogers,

Re: Tactile Device For Push-button Telephones

Thank You for letting us try the above named device.

On trial it was simple to use and will certainly benefit the accuracy

of telephone calls for the Visually handicapped.

It is our opinion that this device will be invaluable to those of us

with a Visual Handicap. It will give us further dignity and independance.

I hope you can successfully convince British Telecom that we need this

simple device.

With Best Wishes for Success,

Katherine Bowman

K. M. Bowman

Gateshead Metropolitan Borough Council

AIRS

ACCESS TO INFORMATION AND READING SERVICES

Co-ordinator: Katherine Bowman.

Central Library · Prince Consort Road
Gateshead · NE8 4LN
Tel: 091 477 3478. Fax 091 477 7454

3 June 1988

Dear Mr Rogers

Re: Identity Plugs

Thank you for letting me see your Braille Identity Plugs. I would fully endorse and encourage these to the Blind community on safety grounds.

Please let me know when they are for sale.

Yours sincerely

Katherine Bowman

Katherine Bowman
Project Co-ordinator

Appendices

Invention Flow Chart: A Guide

Action normally starts at A1 and proceeds through B, C, D etc. Options are circled. If you wish to move out of sequence, locate the section you need, take the advice offered, and then return to the original location. If the invention gets stuck within a section, put it to one side while you work on other ideas.

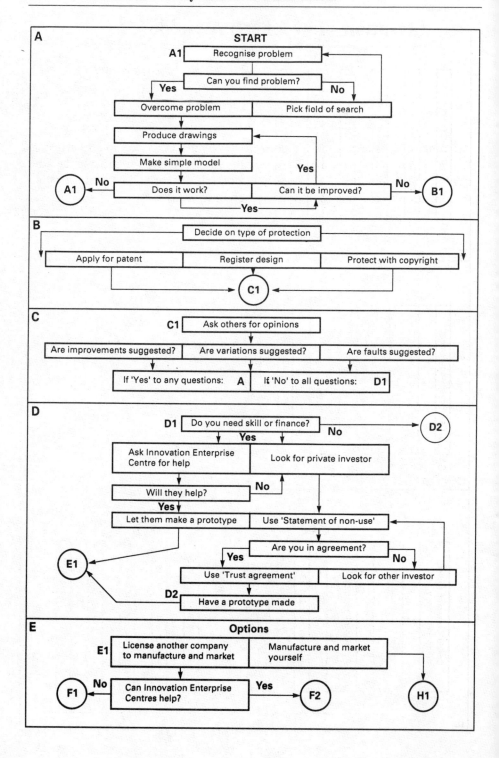

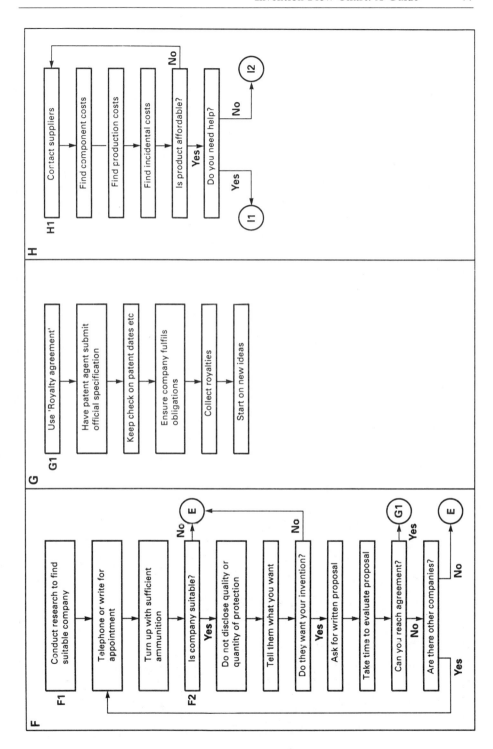

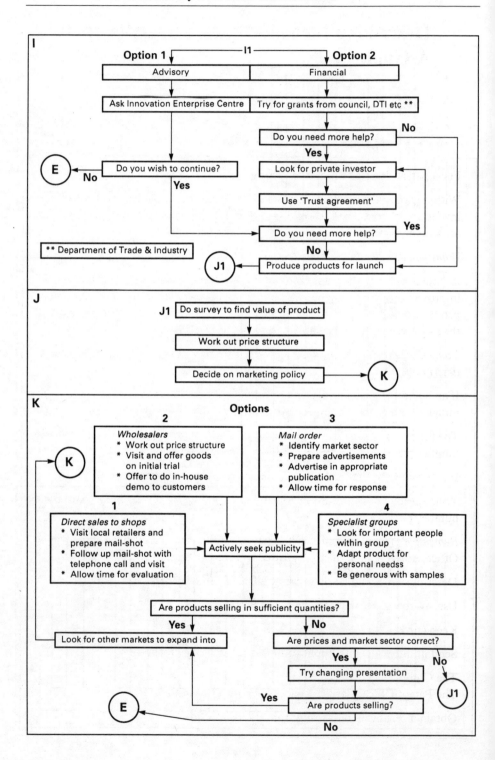

Describing Ideas for Patent Specifications: A Guide

For a patent description to cover your invention the following must apply:

With regard to the invention a person knowledgeable in the field with which the invention is concerned should be able having read the description with accompanying drawings to produce the device so described.

What you describe in your application is what you have protection for.

A patent protects the total combination of features that you describe. If you improve a product by an innovative step and protect that improvement you may produce that product with the improvement even though the product without the improvement may be subject to someone else's patent protection.

You will only be infringing their rights if your improvement is obvious from their description.

If an operating mechanism is incorporated it is acceptable to protect the concept initially leaving aside the mechanism until the final specification is formulated.

The following pages show an example of a DIY patent specification (anti-theft number plate) and simple descriptions of other well-known devices.

It is the concept that is described not the physical appearance.

Your specifications should be expanded as shown by the example 'Anti-theft number plate'.

Remember: Your application will lapse 12 months after it is received at the Patent Office, unless it is by then progressed to the next stage.

Descriptions should be on separate sheets from drawings.

Use A4 sheets, as many sheets as are needed.

Keep copies.

Send in duplicate with application form, fee and fee form to:

The Comptroller
The Patent Office, Cardiff Road, Newport, Gwent NP9 1RH

Obtain a certificate of posting from the post office.

1 of 3

Title of invention

ANTI-THEFT NUMBER PLATE

Area of application

This invention is concerned with vehicle anti-theft devices.

Many devices already exist. However there are various drawbacks.

*Explains existing
drawbacks*

Once a device has been overcome no indication then exists to show that a crime has been committed.

To overcome the problems a plate made from a rigid material has a sliding lockable arm attached to it. The arm is adapted to wrap around the plate to meet another non-moving arm at the plate's rear. The front of the device has the words 'STOLEN IF MOVING' displayed on its front.

The invention will now be further described with reference to the accompanying drawings in which:

*Introduces next
section*

*At least 1" margin
on both sides*

2 of 3

Fig 1 shows a cross-section of the device in use.

Fig 2 shows a front view of the device in use.

*Explains angles of
view of drawings*

According to the invention a plate Fig 2 (a) has a sliding lockable arm (b). A lock (c) is incorporated within the arm.

*Describes device
with reference to
drawings*

In use the device Fig 1 is locked with the moving arm (b) and non-moving arm (a) surrounding and gripping the number plate (d) to a vehicle.

The words 'STOLEN IF MOVING' are then visible at the device's front Fig 2 (a).

*Explains what
invention does*

Using the device has two effects. First, any attempt to remove it by force will damage the number plate, a sure give away to any following vehicle. Second, if the device was left in place, following drivers would know that the vehicle was 'STOLEN'.

*Ties variations to
same concept*

Obviously to one skilled in the arts other means of fixing the device would be obvious and therefore included within the scope of the protection.

*At least 1" margin
at base of text*

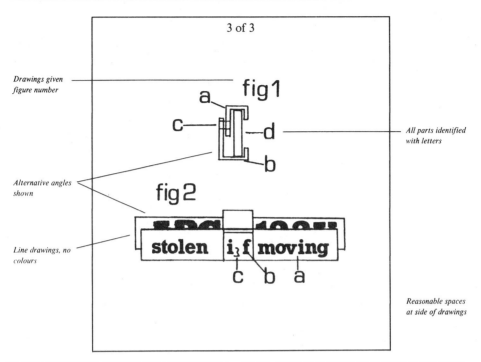

Drawings given figure number

All parts identified with letters

Alternative angles shown

Line drawings, no colours

Reasonable spaces at side of drawings

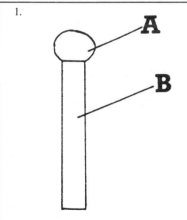

1.

Description: A length of wood or similar flammable material has at one end an ignitable substance fixed thereon (A).

Method: Friction applied to the substance (A) causes it to ignite and subsequently causes the length of flammable material (B) to produce a usable flame.

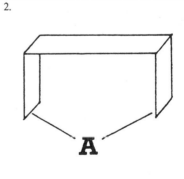

2.

Description: A piece of metal or similarly hard material having both ends bent at 90° and sharpened at their ends (A)

Method: The staple may be used to join two or more materials together by driving its legs through both materials. Folding the legs inwards or outwards forms locking feet.

1–6 Some well-known devices, simply described

3.

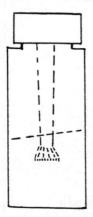

Description: A liquid of any colour that dries rapidly on contact with paper obliterating any writing/print etc beneath it.

Method: Where a printed or written mistake occurs the liquid paper may be used to cover it. New writing or print may be put on to the new surface.

4.

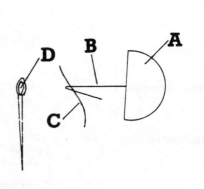

Description: A handle (A) with a flexible spring wire (B) protruding from it.

Method: A length of cotton (C) is looped through the flexible wire (B) and passed through the eye (D) of a needle for easy threading.

5.

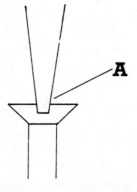

Description: A screwdriver of any known type adapted so that its operative end (A) is magnetic.

Method: In use any screw whether fixed or loose will be drawn to the screwdriver for easy handling.

6.

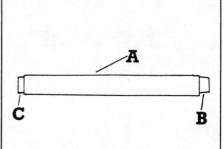

Description: A tube (A) has lead (B) running through its length. A push-button (C) is located within one end of the tube (A).

Method: An internal mechanism (not shown) operated by the push-button (C) propels the lead (B) within the tube along its length and out of its other end.

Specification for British Patent

Title: Lock for push-button telephone

Applicants: R Rogers, of
                  Address:

Inventor: R Rogers, of
                Address:

Priority claim number

First application: 8611488 filed 10 May 1986

Second application: 8612989 filed 28 May 1986

Final application: 8628014 filed 24 November 1986

Description

This invention relates to locks for push-button telephones.

It is often necessary, in both industrial and domestic premises, to prevent unauthorised use of push-button telephones, and there are a variety of telephone key-pad covers and/or locks available for such purposes.

More particularly, these known arrangements commonly enclose all the push-buttons of the key-pad and include a cover having an operative position secured to the body of the telephone or gripping one or more of the push-buttons. Thus the telephone is completely de-activated when the lock is in position thereon.

There are, however, situations where even unauthorised personnel should be in a position to be able to make use of the otherwise inaccessible key-pad of a telephone, for example in the case of an emergency requiring the presence of police, the fire service or the ambulance service, or in other situations internal of the premises where assistance can be gained by dialling a predetermined number.

It would therefore be desirable to be able to provide a lock for a push-button telephone which de-activated the telephone to unauthorised personnel other than in predetermined situations of emergency or where assistance was required.

According to the present invention there is provided a lock for a push-button telephone, the lock comprising a hasp member adapted to be secured to the surface of the key-pad to surround part at least of a predetermined push-button of the key-pad while permitting access through to said push-button, a cover member adapted to encase the remainder of the push-buttons and recessed to receive therethrough said hasp member, and a locking device mounted on the cover member, the locking device including a bolt member having an operative position co-operating with the hasp member to prevent removal of the cover member from the telephone.

It will be appreciated that, with such an arrangement, and with the lock in its operative position on the telephone, the predetermined push-button, conveniently the number 9 key, is always available for use in emergency or like situations, while the other push-buttons are totally inaccessible, thereby preventing unauthorised normal use of the telephone.

Conveniently, the hasp member comprises a base portion having a rectangular aperture therethrough adapted to receive therein the predetermined push-button, and an upstanding abutment portion for co-operation with the bolt member of the locking device.

The base portion of the hasp member may have one or more further rectangular apertures therethrough adapted to receive therein one or more of the push-buttons adjacent to said predetermined push-button.

Preferably, the base portion of the hasp member is secured to the surface of the key-pad of the telephone by means of an adhesive.

The cover member is conveniently of open-bottomed shape including a top wall and depending side walls adapted to seat on the surface of the key-pad, the top wall and the side walls being recessed to receive therethrough the hasp member, the upper end of the abutment portion of the hasp member conveniently being flush with the upper surface of the top wall of the cover member.

The locking device is preferably key-operated and comprises a housing mounted on the cover member, the bolt member being movable in the housing between an inoperative, retracted position remote from the abutment portion of the hasp member and an operative, extended position co-operating with the abutment portion of the hasp member to prevent removal of the cover member from the telephone

In a preferred embodiment of the invention, the abutment portion of the hasp member has a transversely extending slot formed therein, adapted to receive the free end regions of the bolt member in its operative position to effect said co-operation between the locking device and the hasp member.

Conveniently, the bolt member is resiliently biased into its operative position, movement of the bolt member from its operative position to its inoperative position preferably being effected by inserting the key into the locking device to release a locking mechanism reacting between the housing and the bolt member, the key and bolt member then being movable together relative to the housing against said resilient bias.

Although the hasp member and the cover member may be of a plastic material, it is preferred that said components, as well as the locking device, are of die-cast zinc.

By way of example only, an embodiment of the invention will now be described in greater detail with reference to the accompanying drawings of which:

Fig. 1 shows part of a key-pad of a conventional push-button telephone;
Fig. 2 is a perspective view of the cover member and locking device of a telephone lock according to the invention;
Fig. 3 is a perspective view of the hasp member of a telephone lock according to the invention; and
Fig. 4 is a partial vertical section through a telephone lock according to the invention.

Referring to the drawings, Fig. 1 shows a conventional key-pad, indicated generally at 2, of a push-button telephone, the key-pad including a surface 4 through which project push-buttons 6 numbered 0 to 9.

The telephone lock includes a hasp member shown in Fig. 3 and indicated generally at 8, the hasp member 8 comprising a base portion 10 through which are formed a pair of rectangular-shaped apertures 12 and 14 and an open-sided aperture 16. The sizes and spacings of the apertures 12, 14 and 16 conform with those of the push-buttons 6 of the key-pad 2 for reasons which will become apparent.

The hasp member 8 further comprises an upstanding wall 18 between the apertures 12 and 14, said wall 18 having a transverse slot 20 formed in the side thereof adjacent to the aperture 14, again for reasons which will be detailed later.

In the operative position of the illustrated hasp member 8, the base portion 10 is stuck to the surface 4 of the key-pad 2 by means of a strong adhesive with the number 9 push-button passing through the aperture 12 in the base portion 10, with the number 8 push-button passing through aperture 14 in the base portion 10, and with the number 7 push-button passing through the aperture 16 in the base portion, depression of said push-buttons not being prevented by the presence of the hasp member 8.

The telephone lock further includes an open-bottomed cover member indicated generally at 22 and comprising a top wall 24 and depending side walls 26. The cover member 22 is shaped to encase all the push-buttons 6 except the number 9 key, the top wall 24 and side walls 26 being recessed to receive therethrough the upstanding wall 18 of the hasp member 8 and that part of the base portion 10 apertured at 12 and surrounding the number 9 push-button. With the cover member 22 in its operative position seating on the surface 4, the top of the wall 18 of the hasp member 8 is flush with the upper surface of the top wall 24 of the cover member 22.

Mounted on the cover member 22 is a key-operated locking device indicated generally at 28 and including a locking bolt 32. The locking bolt 32 is resiliently biased to the operative position shown in Figs 2 and 4 in which the free end regions of the bolt 32, which include a transverse end flange 34, project outwardly from the housing 30. Movement of the bolt 32 inwardly of the housing 30 from its operative position to a retracted inoperative position is prevented by means of a locking mechanism including spring-loaded locking pins mounted in the housing 30 and reacting between the housing 30 and the locking bolt 32.

Formed in the upper surface of the locking bolt 32 is a keyway 36 in which can be received the shaft 38 of an associated key indicated generally at 40, the arrangement being such that, on insertion of the shaft 38 of the key 40 into the keyway 36 of the bolt 32, the locking pins are urged by the shaft 38 of the key 40 from their locking positions to permit inward movement of the bolt 32 relative to the housing 30. This movement is effected by urging the key inwardly relative to the housing 30 to move the bolt 32 therewith against said resilient bias.

On release of the key the bolt 32 and key 40 are returned by the resilient bias to the operative position of the bolt 32 shown in the drawings.

The described lock operates as follows:

The hasp member 8 is glued into its permanent operative position on the surface 4 of the key-pad 2 with the number 9 push-button projecting through the aperture 12 in the base portion 10 of the hasp member.

The key 40 is inserted into the keyway 36 in the bolt 32, and the cover member 22 and locking device 28 are located over the remaining push-buttons 6 with the upstanding wall 18 projecting through the recess in the cover member 22. The key 40 is pushed inwardly of the housing 30 to urge the bolt 32 into its retracted, inoperative position whereby the cover member 22 can be lowered into its operative position with the side walls 26 engaging the surface 4 of the key-pad 2, the transverse flange 34 on the locking bolt 32 in this inoperative position of the bolt being located to one side of, and out of engagement with, the upstanding wall 18 of the hasp member.

The key 40 is then released and the locking bolt 32 is thus urged outwardly of the housing 30 into its operative position, in which position the end flange 34 on the bolt 32 is received within the transverse slot 20 in the upstanding wall 18 of the hasp member 8.

The key 40 is removed from the bolt 32 and the lock is in its operative position with the co-operation between the end flange 34 of the locking bolt 32 and the slot 20 of the hasp member 8 preventing removal of the cover 22 other than by use of the associated key 40.

Thus normal usage of the telephone is prevented, although emergency use, by way of dialling 999, can still be effected.

The head 42 of the key 40 is angled upwardly relative to the shaft 38 to avoid contact with the hasp member 8 on insertion and removal of the key into and from the keyway 36 and also to indicate the operative orientation of the key – the non-symmetrical nature of such a key adds to the security of the locking device.

Conveniently, the hasp member 8, the cover member 22 and the locking device 28 are die-cast from zinc, although other materials, such as plastics, could be used.

The base portion 10 of the hasp member 8 may be shaped to surround only the predetermined push-button 6, which may be other than the number 9 key, although the greater the area of contact of the hasp member 8 with the surface 4 of the key-pad 2, the more securely can the hasp member be located in its operative position.

In all cases it is to be emphasised that the presence of the hasp member 8 does not in any way detrimentally affect normal depression of the push-buttons 6. Indeed, the permanent presence of the hasp member 8 around a predetermined push-button when the cover member 22 is not in position on the telephone can have distinct advantages in that it positively defines the location of the emergency push-button which can be useful in the event of blackouts or for the non-sighted.

Claims

1. A lock for a push-button telephone, the lock comprising a hasp member adapted to be secured to the surface of the key-pad of the telephone to surround part at least of a predetermined push-button of the key-pad while permitting access therethrough to said push-button, a cover member adapted to encase the remainder of the push-buttons and recessed to receive therethrough the hasp member, and a locking device including a bolt member having an operative position co-operating with the hasp member to prevent removal of the cover member from the telephone.

2. A telephone lock as claimed in claim 1 in which the hasp member comprises a base portion having a rectangular aperture therethrough adapted to receive therein the predetermined push-button, and an upstanding abutment portion for co-operation with the bolt member of the locking device.

3. A telephone lock as claimed in claim 2 in which the base portion of the hasp member has one or more further rectangular apertures therethrough adapted to receive therein one or more of the push-buttons adjacent to said predetermined push-button.

4. A telephone lock as claimed in claim 2 or claim 3 in which the base portion of the hasp member is secured to the surface of the key-pad of the telephone by means of an adhesive.

5. A telephone lock as claimed in any one of claims 2 to 4 in which the cover member is of open-bottomed shape and includes a top wall and depending side walls adapted to seat on the surface of the key-pad, the top wall and side walls being recessed to receive therethrough the hasp member such that the upper end of the abutment portion of the hasp member is flush with the upper surface of the top wall of the cover member.

6. A telephone lock as claimed in any one of claims 2 to 5 in which the locking device is key-operated and comprises a housing mounted on the cover member, the bolt member being movable in the housing between an inoperative retracted position remote from the abutment portion of the hasp member and an extended, operative position co-operating with the abutment portion of the hasp member to prevent removal of the cover member from the telephone.

7. A telephone lock as claimed in claim 6 in which the abutment portion of the hasp member has a transversely extending slot formed therein, adapted to receive the free end regions of the bolt member in its operative position to effect said co-operation between the locking device and the hasp member.

8. A telephone lock as claimed in claim 6 or 7 in which the bolt member is resiliently biased into its operative position.

9. A telephone lock as claimed in claim 8 in which movement of the bolt member from its operative position to its inoperative position is effected by inserting the key into the locking device to release a locking mechanism reacting between the housing and the bolt member, the key and bolt member then being movable together relative to the housing against said resilient bias.

10. A telephone lock as claimed in any one of claims 1 to 9 in which the hasp member, the cover member and the locking device comprise die-cast zinc.

11. A lock for a push-button telephone substantially as described with reference to and as illustrated by the accompanying drawings.

Abstract

A lock for a push-button telephone comprises a hasp member 8 for securing to the surface 4 of the telephone key-pad 2 to surround at least part of a predetermined push-button 6 of the key-pad while still permitting access to that push-button 6, a cover member 22 to encase the remaining push-buttons 6 of the key-pad 2 and having a recess therein to receive the hasp member 8 there-through, and a locking device 28 mounted on the cover member 22 and including a bolt member 32 movable between an inoperative position remote from the hasp member 8 and an operative position co-operating with the hasp member 8 to prevent removal of the cover member 22 from the telephone.

Drawings

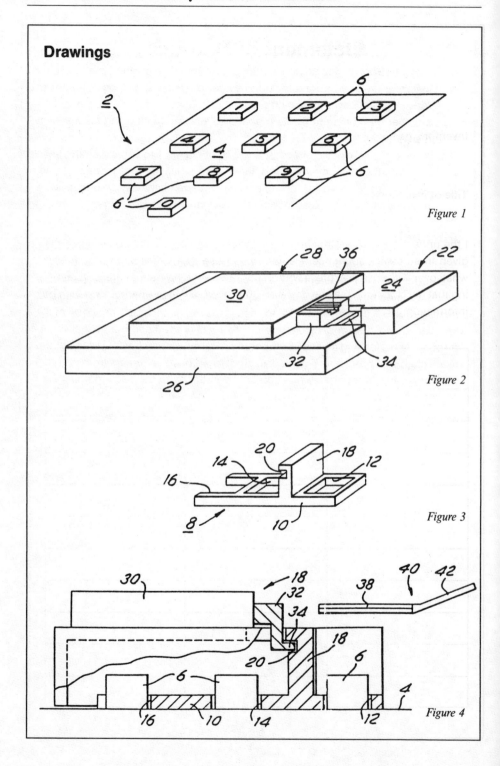

Figure 1

Figure 2

Figure 3

Figure 4

Statement of Non-use

Inventor's name:

Title of invention:

I the undersigned agree that any information given me by the above signed is given in strictest confidence. I agree not to use that information in any way whatsover without the express written permission of the above named. Excepting that my signature shall be declared null and void if I have prior knowledge of information given me by the above signed.

Name	Date	Sign

Declaration of Trust

This declaration of trust is made _____ the _____

_____ 19 _____ by _____ of _____

_____

WHEREAS:

1. The inventor is the inventor/designer of diverse products described herein after _____

2. The inventor wishes to acknowledge the help and assistance given to him/her in the development of the aforesaid products by divesting himself/herself of a percentage of his/her interest in those products

   _____

3. In divesting himself/herself of these percentage interests he/she records that the said percentage interest shall not form part of his income and will subject to the stipulations below become the direct income of the beneficiaries

4. The beneficiaries are:

   (a) _____ of _____

   _____

   (hereinafter called) _____

   (b) _____ of _____

   _____

   (hereinafter called) _____

   (c) _____ of _____

   _____

   (hereinafter called) _____

NOW THIS DEED WITNESSETH as follows:

5. The beneficiaries record that all rights regarding Patent Copyright or Design remain vested in _____ notwithstanding that

improvements in the design cause the product to fall outside the original design or outside the scope of patent protection _____

6. In respect of all products referred to herein a trust account is to be opened within the solicitors firm of _____ of _____ in the joint names of _____ and _____ and all incomes realised by the exploitation of the products shall be paid into that account _____

7. In respect of the product patent application number _____ income in respect thereof shall be paid as to:
    (1)   percent [%]
    (2)   percent [%]
    (3)   percent [%]

8. It being recorded that notwithstanding the beneficiaries are to share in the world-wide income of the application of the patent _____

9. The division of the funds is to take place as follows. That insofar as is practicable all agreements which generate payments are to stipulate that income payments are to be made into the trust account referred to. That the solicitor and the inventor being trustees will within a reasonable time prepare payment statements for the individual beneficiaries herein and will dispatch a statement together with payment to such addresses as the beneficiary shall from time to time record in writing to the firm of solicitors _____. That the inventor and solicitor being trustees may have the right to make such deduction by way of tax or withholding tax or such charges impositions as to taxation VAT or other statutory or quasi-statutory requirements as shall have from time to time been passed

10. It being further recorded that any agreements previously entered into between the parties herein shall be declared null and void _____

IN WITNESS whereof the said _____ has set his hand and seal the day and year first written _____

SIGNED SEALED AND DELIVERED   _____

by the said _____ in   _____

the presence of   _____

Business Plan

Names and addresses of parties concerned.

Rampton Lock

1.00 Introduction

A trend towards increased crime is now well recognised, in particular burglary of industrial premises. This has been established by researching Home Office records held at the local library. Research has also shown that existing lock manufacturing companies are enjoying a good rate of company growth.

Nearly all insurance companies insist that industrial locks comply with specific British Standards. However, standards do not exist with respect to padlocks.

Following discussions with the British Standards Institute it has been found that this is due to the fact that to date, not one padlock manufacturer has been prepared to submit a padlock for testing.

A padlock therefore submitted would have a unique position over other like products, espcially if insurance companies continued with their present policies.

It has been found that the criteria used for the tests are set by the manufacturer submitting the locks for testing.

Following experimentation it has been found that the Rampton Lock as invented by R Rogers has many unique features unavailable in other padlocks. It follows therefore that a set of tests based on those features would make it impossible for any other padlock to come up to what would in effect be the only British Standards for padlocks available.

In this event the retail price of the product would be of secondary importance and more could then be spent on incorporating the unique features involved.

The lock is available to fit a wide range of doors. The complete range is shown in Appendix A.

2.00 Business

2.01 It will be set up as a partnership between Mr and Mrs R Rogers.

2.02 Mr R Rogers aged 37 is an inventor who has been inventing new products for over eight years. He attended Newburn Comprehensive School where he obtained 3 'O' level passes in Maths, English and History. He was employed by Grumits engineering company for five years before they went bust forcing him to become unemployed. He has in the past sold many of his ideas to manufacturing companies but would like now to manufacture and market one of his products himself.

He has completed a business course and obtained a certificate in the following subjects:

Project Planning – Business Finance – Business Planning – Marketing – Selling and Promotion – Premises – Legal Organisation and Raising Finance

2.03 Mrs B Rogers aged 33 is currently holding a secretarial position with a firm of Newcastle-based solicitors. She has been there for five years. Her responsibilities include taking messages, answering letters and arranging appointments.

There are three children aged 14, 12, and 11. Mrs Rogers' sister lives with them and has agreed to take on the day-to-day running of the household.

2.04 **Envisaged responsibilities**
Mr Rogers ... organising components ... assembly ... manpower ... packaging ... marketing.

Mrs Rogers ... running the office ... taking messages ... making appointments ... stock control ... assisting in assembly when necessary.

3.00 **The products**

3.01 *RS1 The rampton lock* ... A seven-lever high-security safe deposit lock mounted in a case-hardened shell is in turn completely surrounded by a cast spherical graphite iron body. Set in the body is a freely revolving hardened steel nose cone. The Rampton Lock can only be used with the Rampton System components. In all cases the locking hasp is slotted into the lock body to form a first 'bond'. The hasp, with the lock attached, is then swung over to conceal the iron staple and form the second 'bond'. A turn of the key locks the whole assembly together.

3.02 *RS2 Padbar assembly* ... For all standard applications. Hasps and staples for the padbar and swing hinge assemblies are made from spherical graphite iron. The hasps have concealed fixing lugs. Within the hinges are two freely rotating stainless steel pins protected top and bottom by 'Armalloy' weld. Both assemblies are supplied with 6 mm backing plates fixing nuts and bolts. Two ball-bearings are supplied for insertion into the fixing lugs to frustrate drilling from the front.

3.03 *RS3 Swing hinge assembly* . . . Fully adjustable from 0 to 2″, the swing hinge allows for uneven surfaces and is ideally suited for sliding doors.

3.04 *RS4 Bolt assembly* . . . Case-hardened 18″ bolt with steel housing and spherical graphite iron staple. Interlocking system allows all components of the bolt assembly to be fitted either vertically or horizontally on door or gate. No fittings are necessary on door surrounds or on gate pillars.

4.00 The market

4.01 It is proposed to sell to locksmiths and DIY stores on a national basis. It is also proposed to sell to local councils, government departments, the armed forces and other end users.

4.02 A huge export market also exists, especially the USA where security seems to be a national obsession.

5.00 Sales and promotion

5.01 There are approximately 2,500 suitable outlets throughout the UK. It is envisaged that each will hold a stock of six Rampton Locks and two each of the padbars, swing hinge and bolt assemblies. The retail value of each outlet's stock will be £400 of which £250 will have been paid to R Rogers's company. The total input from retailers will therefore be £625,000. It is envisaged that each retailer will sell three units per week so early repeat orders are expected.

5.02 There are 120 councils and it is expected to sell five units per month to each of them. This would bring in another £468,000 per annum, bringing the yearly total up to £1,093,000.

5.03 Sales will be promoted through direct visits, articles in trade magazines, promotional exhibitions and by recommendations from insurance companies.

6.00 The premises

6.01 A large industrial unit has been acquired at an Enterprise Centre at Lee Industrial Park, Byker. There is an office and the telephone is connected.

6.02 The rent is £35 per week which includes rates, electricity and heating.

7.00 Financial position

7.01 Mr and Mrs Rogers have £35,000 of available equity in their own home.

7.02 Mr Rogers received £5,000 redundancy of which £3,000 is available for investment in the business.

7.03 Personal banking has been carried out at Barclays Bank, Westgate Road, Fenham for five years without recourse to borrowing over the last three years.

7.04 There are no outstanding HP commitments.

7.05 Funding requirements for the next two years' sales as shown in Appendix B can be summarised as follows;

Investment
Working capital	£47,490
Fixed assets	£16,905
Rent	£ 3,640
Total	£68,035

Source of funds
Proprietor's funds	£32,000
Bank loan	£30,000
HP	£ 5,000
Grants	£ 3,000
Total	£70,000

8.00 Staff

8.01 In the first year one full-time assembler and three part-time workers. Also home workers as and when needed.

8.02 In the second year a further four full-time workers may be required.

8.03 Extra part-time workers will be used if necessary.

8.04 A full schedule of wages is shown in Appendix C.

9.00 Costs

9.01 It is calculated that there will be a gross profit of 70 per cent throughout the range of products.

10.00 Suppliers

10.01 The castings will be obtained from Acme Castings Ltd.

10.02 The internal lock mechanism will be obtained from Taylor Locks.

11.00 Equipment

11.01 A schedule of required assets with value are shown in Appendix D.

12.00 Time-scale

12.01 The premises are available for immediate occupation.

12.02 The casting moulds can be finished in five weeks.

12.03 It is expected that trading will commence 1 July 1986.

Appendix A – Range of locks

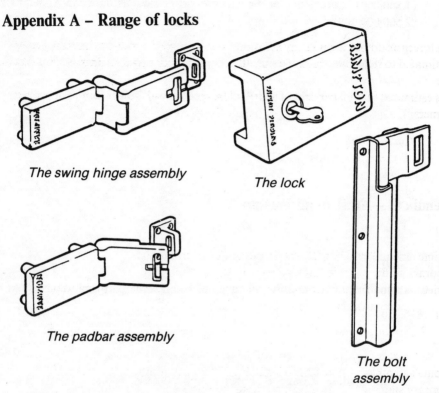

The swing hinge assembly

The lock

The padbar assembly

The bolt assembly

- Completely integrated staple and hasp locking system.
- All external components made from spherical graphite iron – well known for tremendous strength and malleability.
- Design is clean, seamless and interlocking – no part of the Rampton is vulnerable to specific attack.
- Bolt-croppers cannot bite and battering only produces noise.
- No place for a lever or Jemmy to get any purchase.
- Seven-lever safe-type locking system virtually unpickable.
- Unique re-set feature – authorised user can re-set to a different key in seconds. User can also set to own master key. If key is compromised only the key needs replacing – not the lock.
- Security ensured – not even the installer will know the key.
- Suitable for both heavy duty external and internal use.
- Complete system, padbar, swing hinge or bolts all designed to take the Rampton Lock.

Appendix B – Sales

Forecast sales for three years:

1986	£1,093,000
1987	£1,850,000
1988	£2,500,000

These forecasts do not include any additions to the range or products. Increased sales are estimated to reflect the market trend, 10 per cent inflation and an increased market share.

It is estimated that 60 per cent of sales will be retailed with 40 per cent to approved customers.

Appendix C – Staff requirements

Year 1

Full-time assembler: 1 at £3,600 including NI contributions
Temporary staff: 3 at £1.80p per hour = £6,120
Proprietor's annual drawings £6,000 including tax and class 4 NI contributions

Total: £15,720

Year 2

Full-time assembler: 4 at £3,960 including NI contributions
Temporary staff: 3 at £1.98p per hour = £9,180
Proprietor's annual drawings £6,750 including tax and class 4 NI contributions

Total: £31,770

Appendix D – Equipment requirements

Asset	Value	Purchase	Depreciation	
Motor vehicle	£ 5,000	HP over three years 25% deposit	25%	£1,250
Casting tool	£ 7,000	Cash	10%	£ 700
Assembly tables	£ 200	Cash	10%	£ 20
Shelving, etc	£ 400	Cash	10%	£ 40
Office equipment	£ 1,200	Cash	10%	£ 120
Special tools	£ 600	Cash	10%	£ 60
Sprayer	£ 300	Cash	10%	£ 30
Subtotal	£14,700			£2,220
VAT at 15%	£ 2,205			
Total	£16,905			

Depreciation calculated on 'straight-line basis'.

Summary of financial assumptions used in plan

1. Sales: percentage of turnover: Rampton Lock 50%
    Padbar 25%
    Swing hinge 25%
    Bolt 25%
2. Gross margin: 70%
3. Customers: Cash . . . credits (30 days)
4. Depreciation: As in Appendix D
5. VAT: 15%
6. Stocks: 3 months of planned sales
7. Property: Rented
8. Bank interest: 15% per annum
9. Staff wages: As in Appendix C
10. Council rates: Inclusive with rent
11. HP: As in Appendix D
12. Total own capital introduced: £32,000

Royalty Payment Agreement

1. Parties

_____ of

_____

_____ ('the company') (1)

[   ] of [   ]

[   ]   ('the inventor') (2)

2. The definitions: The following terms shall have the following meanings in this agreement.

2.1 The patents
Patent application number: [   ].

2.2 The products
[   ] the subject of the patents and any agreement by virtue of any of the provisions of this agreement.

2.3 The licensee

_____ of

_____

_____ ('the company') (1)

2.4 The licensor

[   ] of [   ]

[   ]   ('the inventor') (2)

2.5 The licence
A licence of even date made between the company (1) and the licensor (2).

2.6 The term
The period from the date hereof to the expiry of the last patent relating to the products unless sooner determined as provided in the conditions.

2.7   The territory
[   ]   [   ]   [   ]

2.8   Gross sales
The price as duly invoiced or chargeable to customers by the company in respect of all goods sold before deduction of cash discounts and commissions (except trade discounts) but excluding purchase sales import or value added tax.

2.9   The business
The business of manufacture sale and distribution of the products in the territory during the term.

2.10   The royalty
[   ] per cent [%] of the gross sales of the business in the territory during the term in respect of the products sold or distributed by the licensee itself or any member of the group of companies of which it is a member in each year of the term.

2.11   The payment dates
The 31 January, the 30 April, the 31 July, the 31 October, in each year of the term.

2.12   The agreement
In consideration of the payment of the royalty by the licensee to the licensor and of the subject to the agreements on the part of the licensee in this agreement the licensor HEREBY GRANTS to the licensee the exclusive right (i) of using the patents (ii) in the business (iii) within the territory (iv) for the term.

2.13   The conditions
The standard conditions consisting of . . . signed pages and special conditions (if any) also signed annexed hereto shall be deemed to be incorporated in this agreement in their entirety.

[DATED THIS _____ DAY OF _____ 19 _____

Signed by
For and on Behalf of
[_____]   [....................................]
                                                                    Authorised signatory
              Witnessed by   [...................................]

Signed by
For and on Behalf of
[_____]   [....................................]
                                                                    Authorised signatory
              Witnessed by   [...................................]

Standard Conditions

1. The licensor warrants that it is the sole beneficial owner of the patents and is entitled to enter into this agreement.

2. The licensor agrees as follows:
    (a) to apply promptly for registration of patents in the territory when due at the expense of the licensee in the term;
    (b) to notify the licensee of any improvements in the products which come to the attention of the licensor and to permit the licensee to use such improvements without further charge;
    (c) not to grant any licence or other right (by act or omission) to any third party within the territory in any way.

3. The licensee agrees throughout the term:
    (a) to apply promptly for registration of patents in the territory when due at the expense of the licensee in the term;
    (b) to commence the business immediately;
    (c) to apply for all necessary government consents in respect of this agreement;
    (d) to arrange fully comprehensive public liability and employer's liability insurance with a substantial insurer in the territory for the products prior to any sale or other distribution of the products;
    (e) to procure that the licensor is also covered by such insurance policy;
    (f) to pay promptly the insurance premium in respect of the policy whenever due;
    (g) not to employ any person in the business until such person has signed a non-disclosure undertaking in the form approved by the licensor from time to time.

4. The licensee also agrees throughout the term:
    (a) to procure the greatest volume of business for the business and the products consistent with high quality;
    (b) not to engage in any activities which may be contrary to government or other regulation;
    (c) to pay the royalty in the currency (without demand deduction or set-off) to the licensor (or as it directs) on each of the payment dates.

5. To calculate the royalties on the gross sales of the products in the business in the territory during each calendar quarter of the term (and for any period less than a complete calendar quarter) and gross sales shall include:
    (a) all credit sales of whatever nature whether or not the licensee has received payment of the outstanding account by the payment date relevant

to the quarter when such credit sales were made;

(b) all cash sales made but not invoiced by the licensee in each quarter;

(c) all products sold or delivered during each quarter which are unpaid and not invoiced on the relevant payment dates;

(d) all products sold or otherwise disposed of in any manner whatsoever in the territory during each quarter but shall exclude any customer refunds or credits arising from the supply of defective products provided that such refunds or credits shall only be deducted from gross sales in the calendar quarter in which they are paid or allowed to the customer.

6. On each of the payment dates to furnish to the licensor complete and accurate statements (in the form approved by the licensor) of the gross sales stock and purchases of the business since the last payment date.

7. To keep accurate books and accounts of the business and the products in accordance with good accountancy custom in the territory and:

(a) have them audited once a year during the term by a qualified auditor and submit the whole of such audited accounts to the licensor within three months of the end of each year;

(b) keep them for not less than three years;

(c) permit the licensor to inspect and take copies (at the expense of the licensor) of any financial information or records it requires (on reasonable prior notice in the event of inspection after normal working hours).

8. In the event of discrepancies (amounting in total to more than 2 per cent per annum) in any such books or accounts to permit independent accountants at the expense of the licensor to undertake audits of the same in each year of the term for the licensor (at intervals at the discretion of the licensor) on reasonable notice during normal working hours.

9. Not to conduct the business in respect of the product except:

(a) under proper and comprehensive financial systems and controls as approved or stipulated by the licensor;

(b) inside the territory;

(c) in respect of the products which confirm to all relevant government or other regulations.

10. To permit the licensor or its representatives to inspect all premises for the purposes of the business at any time during the term and to take stock checks of all materials stored there or elsewhere at other premises under the control of the licensee and to make such other investigations as may be necessary in the opinion of the licensor to ensure that the products are of high quality.

11. To affix such patent, copyright or trade mark ownership notices to the

products and any stationery packaging or advertising associated with the business or the products as the licensor requires.

12. To indemnify the licensor from:
(a) any unauthorised use or infringement of any patent, trade mark, copyright or other intellectual property by the licensee;
(b) any claim by any third party in respect of the conduct of the business or the products or the conduct or neglect of the licensee;
(c) any infringement by the licensee of any relevant regulations.

13. Not to grant any sub-licence without the consent of the licensor.

14. Not to assign transfer or otherwise deal with the right or this agreement or the business in any way without the prior consent of the licensor.

15. As (in the case of a corporate licensee) this licence has been granted to the licensee by the licensor in reliance upon the quality of the directors and shareholders of the licensee any change in the same shall be subject to the prior approval of the licensor.

16. The licensee further agrees throughout the term:
(a) to make such improvements to the products as are required from time to time and notwithstanding the said improvements shall continue to pay the royalties to the licensor notwithstanding that the improvements or some total thereof might by themselves or in accumulation mean that the licensee could assert that the patents or any of them have been superseded by the improvements to the products.
(b) not to promote or manufacture any products that are in direct competition with the products herein which are the subject of the patents referred to in paragraph 2.1 of this agreement.
(c) whenever reasonably required by the licensor to defend or procure the defence of any challenge to the validity of the patents and at the expense of the licensee take proceedings against infringers of the patents and:
   (i) in respect of any damages awarded by the court and recovered to pay one-half thereof to the licensor or:
   (ii) in respect of sums agreed by compromise to obtain the consent of the licensor to such compromise and thereafter to pay one-half of those damages to the licensor. Save that the licensee shall be re-imbursed from the damages the reasonable legal fees and disbursements expended in pursuing the action.

17. The licensee further agrees throughout the term:
(a) on termination of this agreement:
(b) to forthwith cease the business and:

(c) four weeks prior to the expiry of the term or three weeks after receipt of notice of this agreement to furnish to the licensor complete and accurate up-to-date stock check with estimates of turnover of the business in respect of the sale of the products to such date of expiry or termination and thereupon to pay the continuing royalties on such estimated turnover to such date and not later than the first quarter day after such date to pay to the licensor any additional amount of the continuing royalties calculated on actual gross sales of the business in respect of the products to such date.

18. And for a period of one year thereafter:
    (a) not to engage directly or indirectly in any capacity in any business venture competitive or in conflict with the business in the territory;
    (b) not to solicit the customers or former customers of the business with the intent of taking their custom;
    (c) not to employ any employees or former employees who are employed in the business by the licensee or by the licensor or any other licensee of the licensor, and to procure that all directors and shareholders of a corporate licensee enter into direct covenants of similar context with the licensor.

19. To notify the licensor and provide full details of any improvements and the method systems or equipment employed in the business and to permit the licensor to incorporate free of charge any such improvements in its know-how for the benefit of the licensor and all its licensees.

20. Not without prior consent of the licensor to deal with the products:
    (a) except through normal retail or wholesale outlets of repute;
    (b) to any entity which intends to dispose of or use (directly or indirectly) any of the products for gratuitous or subsidised distribution for publicity, promotional, advertising or premium purposes or for sales incentive schemes or for any other such purpose.

21. Not to sell or otherwise deal with the products without first submitting not less than six samples of a proposed product with packaging and advertising associated with the products to the licensor and to ensure that all the products confirm to sample.

22. On demand to supply any of the products to the licensor or as it directs at the lowest price at which such products are dealt in by the licensee with priority to the licensor.

23. It is further agreed between the parties:
    (a) all rights not specifically and expressly granted to the licensee in this agreement are reserved to the licensor.

24. The licensor may grant a licence to any entity in the territory to manufacture any of the products in the territory for use in connection with the business or for other purposes (except in competition with the licensee in the territory) without liability to the licensee.

25. All sums due to the licensor which are not paid on the due date (without prejudice to the rights of the licensor and the conditions that the royalties are paid time being of the essence) shall bear interest from day to day at the annual rate of 4 per cent above the current Barclays Bank Limited London daily base interest rate for sterling with a minimum of 12 per cent per annum.

26. The receipt of moneys by the licensor shall not prevent either of the parties questioning the correctness of any statement of those moneys nor shall be a waiver of any of its rights or claims against the licensee.

27. Both parties shall be released from their respective obligations in the event of national emergency, war, prohibitive government regulations or if any other cause beyond the control of the parties shall render performance of this agreement impossible whereupon:
    (a) all the royalties due shall be paid immediately, and
    (b) the licensee shall forthwith cease the business
    provided that this clause shall only have effect at the discretion of the licensor except when such event renders performance impossible for a continuous period of 12 calendar months.

28. In the event that any provisions of this agreement or these conditions are void, voidable or illegal the parties shall amend that provision in such reasonable manner as achieves the intention of the parties wihout illegality.

29. The licensor may in its sole discretion determine this agreement on 30 days' notice in the event that:
    (a) any necessary government or bank consent is not forthcoming, or
    (b) substantial dealings with the products in the territory are not made within six months of the date of this agreement or for a continuous period of six months during the term.

30. The expiration or termination of this agreement shall not relieve either of the parties of their respective obligations prior thereto or impair or prejudice their respective rights against the other.

31. No exercise of discretion, judgment, opinion or approval of any matter mentioned in this agreement or arising from it shall be deemed to have been made by the licensor except if in writing and shall be at its sole discretion

otherwise provided in this agreement or these conditions.

32. Any notice to be served on either of the parties by the other shall be sent by pre-paid recorded delivery or registered post (as the case may be) or by telex/fax if both parties have a telex/fax machine and shall be deemed to have been received by the addressee within 12 hours if sent by telex/fax to the correct telex/fax number of the addressee.

33. Each of the parties shall notify the other of any change of address or number within 24 hours of such change.

34. The parties are not partners or joint venturers nor is the licensee able to act as the agent or to pledge the credit of the licensor in any way.

35. The licensee acknowledges that this agreement and these conditions are the whole agreement between the parties and has not relied upon any oral representations made to it by the licensor or its employees or representatives or agents and has made its own independent investigations into all matters relevant to the business.

36. In the event the licensee fails to observe or peform any of its obligations under this agreement or these conditions in any way then the licensor may terminate this agreement on 30 days' written notice and:
    (a) if the breach complained of is incapable of remedy this agreement shall terminate on service of such notice;
    (b) in every other case if the breach complained of is remedied to the satisfaction of the licensor within the notice period this agreement shall not terminate;
    (c) no waiver of any breach of those obligations shall constitute a waiver of any further or continuous breach of the same.

37. If the licensee enters into liquidation or bankruptcy or suffers a receiver to be appointed to it or to any of its assets or makes a composition with any of its creditors (or the equivalent in Scotland) the licensor may at any time thereafter terminate this agreement on notice with immediate effect and:

38. No creditor or agent representative or trustee of the licensee shall have the right to use the knowledge or continue the business without the consent of the licensor until payment of all monies due to the licensor from the licensee on any account. The licensor:
    (a) shall have a lien on any of the stock or other products concerned with the business not then disposed of by the licensee in respect of the business;
    (b) the property in any goods supplied by the licensee to the licensor shall remain with the licensor.

39. The licensor may assign, charge or otherwise deal with this agreement in any way.

40. Marginal notes by these conditions are for reference purposes only and shall not be incorporated in this agreement or these conditions and shall not be deemed to be any indication of the meaning of the clauses to which they relate.

41. English law only shall apply to this agreement and the English Courts shall have sole jurisdiction.

Some Useful Publications

From the Patent Office

Patent Protection

How to Prepare a UK Patent Application

Design Registration

Registering a Trade or Service Mark

From main public libraries

The United Kingdom Patents Act 1977, Hugh Brett

From Kogan Page

Law for the Small Business: The Daily Telegraph Guide, 7th Edition (1991), Patricia Clayton

A complete list of Kogan Page titles for business and management is available from the publishers at 120 Pentonville Road, London N1 9JN; tel: 071-278 0433.

Useful Addresses

The Patent Office
Filing of documents, general enquiries and publications
Patent Office
25 Southampton Buildings
London WC2A 1AY
Hours: 10am to 4pm Monday to Friday (except public holidays)
Tel: 071-438 4724/4701/4702/4704

Filing of documents and fees by post, publications
Patent Office
Cardiff Road
Newport
Gwent NP9 1RH
Hours: 10am to 4pm Monday to Friday (except public holidays)
Tel: 0633 814000

Search and Advisory Service
The Patent Office
Hazlitt House
45 Southampton Buildings
Chancery Lane
London WC2A 1AR
Tel: 071-438 4747/8
Fax: 071-438 4750

Chartered Institute of Patent Agents
Staple Inn Buildings
London WC1V 7PZ
Tel: 071-405 99450

Department of Trade and Industry
Industrial Property & Copyright Department
1–19 Victoria Street
London SW1H 0ET
Tel: 071-829 6944 (Patents)
     071-829 6020 (Copyright)

The Design Council
28 Haymarket
London SW1 4SU
Tel: 071-839 8000

Designs Registry
Telephone or personal enquiries
Designs Registry
Patent Office
Chartist Tower
Upper Dock Street
Newport
Gwent NP9 1DW
Hours: 10am to 4pm Monday to Friday (except public holidays)
Tel: 0633 814000 X5162

European Patent Office
Erhardtstrasse 27
D-8000 München 2

Institute of Trade Mark Agents
4th Floor
Canterbury House
2–6 Sydenham Road
Croydon
Surrey CR0 9XD
Tel: 081-686 2052

Public Record Office
Ruskin Avenue
Kew
Richmond
Surrey TW9 4DU
Tel: 081-876 3444

Science Reference and Information Service
25 Southampton Buildings
London WC2A 1AW
Hours: 9.30am to 9pm Mondays to Fridays (except public holidays)
10am to 1pm Saturdays
Tel: 071-323 7494

World Intellectual Property Organisation
34 Chemin des Colombettes
CH-1211 Geneva 2

Index

add = address